PLANTS

of
TROPICAL
NORTH
QUEENSLAND

THE COMPACT GUIDE

b
John B

GW00673371

ISBN 1 876617 13 6

Cover Design by John Beasley
Photography by John Beasley
Text & book design by John Beasley
Maps by Footloose Maps

Cover Photograph – Kahlpahlim Rock

For further information please contact
John Beasley
Phone - 07 4093 0303
E-mail – beasley@austarnet.com.au

Published by Footloose Publications
PO Box 837 Kuranda
Qld 4881 Australia

June 2006

WARNING
MANY NATIVE FRUITS IN NORTH QUEENSLAND ARE POISONOUS.
DO NOT RISK EATING OR TASTING THEM,
AS EVEN SMALL AMOUNTS CAN BE DANGEROUS.

CONTENTS

FOREWORD

This book is for everyone interested in the plants of Far North Queensland. It assists with identification of some 485 plants from the area around Cairns including Cardwell, Chillagoe and Cooktown. Of course, many of the plants included are found across a much larger area. There is a special focus on the area's primitive plants (See p189).

Designed as a compact guide, the book uses several methods of locating and identifying a plant.

Photographs are provided for all plants, focussing on characteristic features.
Simple keys allow a rapid search based on prominent features of a plant.
Common name and scientific name indices are provided at the end of the book.
Plants are broadly grouped according to the dominant ecosystems of the area.
Within those groups, plants are arranged by type, such as trees, shrubs, vines, etc.
Where feasible, related plants are listed together, eg figs, eucalypts, wattles, and so on.
Reference is made to related plants in other sections of the book.

To achieve the maximum information in a book that will fit comfortably into a backpack has necessitated small print and some abbreviations. Most entries include the following:

Number Common Name (Weed) (Butterfly Plant) (Primitive Plant)
Scientific Name   Then a brief introductory description.
Geographical range of the plant, locally, and throughout Australia and the world.
General information about the plant, such as commercial, Aboriginal, or medicinal uses.
Quirky information from the internet, where appropriate. (Look for words like 'supposedly' and 'reputedly')
Specific information: height, leaflet/leaf size, times of flowering and fruiting.

While this book has been designed for local residents wanting to know what grows in their own backyards, and visitors to the area with an interest in plants, it may also be of some assistance to those with a more specialised interest in plants.

Thanks

To my friends Bruce Wannan, Reinhild Tracey, and Andrew Horn, who assisted with my education in the complex world of tropical plants which I entered in writing this book. Although I wanted the book to be simple and easy for non-botanists to use, it is not so easy to reach that ideal without the assistance of specialists in this field, and I am grateful for the time and resources they so willingly gave to me.

To Bob Jago, who kindly agreed to look through my draft manuscript, correcting some of the more blatant errors. Bob's knowledge of and ability to identify the plants of North Queensland is unsurpassed.

To my wife, Ruth, and to Jim Kinley, Reinhild Tracey, and Bruce Wannan for accompanying me on walks to gather information and photographs. Jim in particular was a patient accomplice on various missions to search out information. My special thanks go to Ruth for her unfailing support and encouragement throughout the project.

To Kym Dungey and Jane Whytlaw, of Footloose Publications, who assisted with the preparation of the draft manuscript for printing, and with distribution of my books. I knew the quality of their 'Tropical Walking Tracks' books and I have been fortunate to have their help with this book.

I wish to acknowledge the assistance of Jo Wynter from Nature's Powerhouse, Cooktown, Sandy Lloyd from the Cooktown Botanic Gardens, Ellen Terrell of Daintree, and Bruce and Kath Hinchley of Cardwell, who have all made my task easier.

While I have gladly accepted information from many sources, the responsibility for any errors remains with me. I would appreciate feedback from readers of this book, with their suggestions for improvements or corrections.

Photography

Most photographs in this book were taken by the author on a 4 mega pixel Canon PowerShot A85 digital camera or a 5 mega pixel Canon PowerShot S2 1S digital camera. Thanks to Kym Dungey for the use of his photographs (for plant nos 365 & 368). The text records credits for a small number of other borrowed photographs.

Bibliography

While I referred to many books and other resources while researching this book, I would like to acknowledge the following, which I found particularly useful. Readers seeking more information may also find them helpful.

'Tropical Walking Tracks' by Kym Dungey and Jane Whytlaw, (Footloose Publications)
      (The ideal companion volume to this book. Accurate and affordable information for walkers.)
'Fruits of the Australian Rainforest' by Wendy and William T. Cooper, (Nokomis, Melbourne, 2004)
      (Beautifully illustrated and a work of up-to-date scholarship, this is the nearest thing to a botany of Far North Queensland. I found it indispensible.)
'Australian Ferns and Fern Allies' by D.L. Jones and S.C. Clemesha, (Reed Books, NSW, 1980)
      (An older but still useful book, with good B&W illustrations.)
'Field Guide to Eucalypts - Volume 3' by Brooker & Kleinig, (Inkata Press, Chatswood, 1994)
      (Still a very useful guide to the Eucalypts of Northern Australia, and well illustrated.)
'Wood in Australia' by Keith R. Bootle, (McGraw -Hill, Sydney, 1983)
      (An excellent guide to the variety of timbers used in Australia.)
'What to Plant - An Illustrated guide for Australian Gardeners' by K. Pienaar & D. Greig, (Angus & Robertson, 1984)
      (A compendium of indigenous and introduced plants for Australian gardens, well illustrated.)
'Australian Tropical Rainforest Plants - Trees, Shrubs and Vines' by B.P.M. Hyland, T. Whiffin, D.C. Christophel, B. Gray & R.W. Elick, (CSIRO, computer disc, 2002)
      (Awkward to use, but an invaluable botanical resource, with specialised leaf photography.)

How to use this Guide

To Identify a Plant

Turn first to the **keys** on pages 6 -9. Find the characteristic most likely to identify the plant you are examining. (For example - Red flowers.) Look for sub-categories within the key that suit the plant. (For example - Trees with red flowers.) Note the list of **plant identification numbers**. (These are not page numbers, which have been kept unobtrusive.)

Now turn to the numbered list of plants that make up the body of this book. Look up the plant identification numbers taken from the key. If the plant you are examining is in this guide, there may be other characteristics listed which will assist you to confirm the identification. In some cases similar plants, and the characteristics which allow you to tell them apart, will be listed. Often the photograph will be enough to make a quick identification.

To Locate a Plant

If you wish to locate a specimen of a plant listed in this book, in some cases a location has been noted. The **map** on p186 may assist, or you may refer to the ideal companion to this guide, Kym Dungey and Jane Whytlaw's "Tropical Walking Tracks", to plan a walk. The grouping of plants also assists location; by identifying the type of vegetation in which you are walking you can then turn to that section of the book to look for other species.

The Scope of this Guide

The aim of this book is to allow you to identify plants in the Cairns region which are likely to attract your attention. Since there are over 1000 species of trees alone in the rainforest of the Wet Tropics region (compared with 35 native tree species for the whole of the United Kingdom), only a small proportion of these can be listed. This guide focusses on those plants that stand out to an interested observer in some way, and the keys have been built around those characteristics that make the plant noteworthy in the first place. While a wide range of plants is included, from ferns to grasses to large trees, the main emphasis is on larger plants and trees, both native and introduced species. A number of the attractive street trees found in Cairns are included, but garden plants are generally not listed. With palms, only Australian species are listed. Further information about each plant has been included, as outlined in the Foreword on page 3.

The language used and the characteristics identified in this book do not require special botanical knowledge or equipment, but some general knowledge of plants is assumed. Botanists deal with mature foliage from the crown of a tree when making identifications. This guide often refers to juvenile plants, since they are accessible and more likely to be noticed. However you should be aware that many rainforest trees have very different leaves at different stages of growth, and sometimes even on the same tree. Other plants have quite different forms depending on where they are growing. Where possible the guide will refer to these variations, but you are entering some of the most complex ecosystems on our planet, and this compact guide can only hope to be an introduction to that complexity.

Naming plants is fraught with difficulties. Common names vary from person to person, and some names refer to more than one plant, while even the scientific names are constantly being reviewed and amended. Since common names are easier to use initially, most plants in this book are referred to by a common name in use in the area. The scientific name is given in *italics*, in the usual form with the genus first and capitalised, the species following in lower case. Where the species is not known or not yet finalised, the abbreviation *sp* is used. Where possible this guide identifies the species of plant, but in some cases only the family name is given.

Do read the notes on harmful plants (nos 1-4), especially if you are new to the area, and remember that many rainforest fruits are extremely poisonous to us, even if eaten by some animals or birds. Most walking tracks are in World Heritage listed areas, and the plants are protected. Please do your best to conserve them. Good luck with your identifications.

John Beasley

The Keys

● Red   Plant Numbers

RED FLOWERS   Trees   -fluffy flowers   39 44 96 436 481
       -massed flowers 16 41 237 253 257 276 468 476
       -simple flowers 50 244 258 469
       Other Plants   19 70 72 85 86 158 172 318 322 427 459 466
RED FRUIT   Trees   -figs   103-5 223 225 233 384
       -globular fruit   37 43 52 188 189 250 263 348 349
       -pods   100 102 110
       -other fruit   1 32 36 48 108 135 243 245 262 439 441 444
       Other Plants   -palms   61 278-9 281-2
       -vines   301 303 309 313-4 317 320 324 417
       -all other fruit   59 70 78 85 145 198 329 336-7 339 344 361 363-4 405-6
RED LEAVES   Trees   31 40 118 202 209 254-5 257 259 390 435 438 440
(+new growth)   Other Plants   305-7 451 466
RED BARK   Trees   36 202 247 260 267 393 395 399
(+stems)   Other Plants   29 149 347 409 480

◯ Pink

PINK FLOWERS   Trees   39 53 114 236 258 436 438 469 472 475 479 481-2 484-5
       Other Plants -shrubs   56 140-1 149 150 178 322 407 411 456
       -vines   154 161-2 178 318 325 417 463 477
       -all other plants 72 165 168 177 432-4 450-1 460
PINK FRUIT   Trees   -figs   105 224 232 384
       -all other trees   1 31 122 124 129 135 207 439 442
       Other Plants   21 63 145 156 406
PINK LEAVES   All Plants   133 259 293 299 306-7 322 390   *(including new growth)*
PINK BARK OR STEMS   All Plants   1 29 185 270 373

◯ Orange

ORANGE FLOWERS   Trees   7 50 96 115 125 199 276 370 378 437 478
       Other Plants   19 141 164 166 172 178 350 461
ORANGE FRUIT   Trees -figs   225 229-30 233
       -all other trees   7 10 48 52 100 108 111-2 116 121 124 128 194 214 243
       250-2 274 390
       Other Plants -vines   152 160 280 304 319 324 362
       -all other plants 54 59 61 78 80-1 139 327-8 351 364 413 431
ORANGE LEAVES   All Plants   40 202 209 221 272 307 357   *(including new growth)*

◯ Yellow

YELLOW   Trees   -fluffy flowers   34-6 97-8 100-1 191-2 396 474
FLOWERS   -all other trees   36 49 50 109 113 242 382 391 400 470-1 474 483
       Other Plants -shrubs   58 141 147 402-4 480
       -all other plants 28 74 148 164 166 177 179-80 309 324 338 429 458 464-5
YELLOW FRUIT   Trees   43 103-4 111 116 121 123 225-6 228 383-4 400 445
       Other Plants   2-4 20 68 80 155 280 338 462

● Brown (and Beige)

BROWN FLOWERS   All Plants   28 154 164 182 193 312
BROWN FRUIT   Trees -pods   34-5 53 97-9 110 191-2 199 205 253 366 396 438 468 471
       -all other trees   31 113 258 262 370 *(Partial list - this is a common colour)*
       Other Plants   18 67 157 308 325 360 402 403

The Keys

○ Cream   **Plant Numbers**

CREAM FLOWERS Trees -fluffy flowers 34 47 88 97-9 101 191-2 373 376
　　　　　　　　　　　 -all other trees 6 37 48 127 166 196 208 243 328 379 444

◉ Blue

BLUE FLOWERS	All Plants	181 340-3 428 452-3 457 462
BLUE FRUIT	Trees	33 38 40 117-8 204 248 262
	Other Plants	181 269 330 345 347 359

○ Mauve

| MAUVE FLOWERS | Trees | 116 473 484 |
| | Other Plants | 140 142 162 177 317 326 426 455 462 463 |

● Purple

PURPLE FLOWERS	Trees	53 473 484
	Other Plants	65 140 142 161 171 181 317 340-1 343 353 417 453 477 480
PURPLE FRUIT	Trees -figs	227 230 232 384
	-all other trees	5 32-3 117 126 136 201 207 235 240-1 248 260 267-8
	Other Plants	181 343
PURPLE STEMS/LEAVES	All Plants	1 29 264 266 275 407 463

◉ Green

GREEN FLOWERS	Trees	38 42 44 46 208 243 396
	Other Plants	147 151 269 319 449
GREEN FRUIT *(Ripe)*	Trees	5-6 8 9-13 15 30 38 50 114 133 223 226 231 236 245-6 264
	Other Plants	142 157 334 367 409

○ White

WHITE FLOWERS Trees	-single flowers	5-6 114 120 122 134 243 262 333 371 372 388
	-fluffy flowers	38 45-6 87 89-95 200 373-5 387 389 439-41
	-spikes	30 32-3 195 197 256 273 379-80
	-all other trees	9 14-5 42 131 193 202-6 208 210 216 219-20 274 444 469
Other Plants	-vines	150 152-3 301 303 308 313-4 316 321 326 414 417 419
	-shrubs	22 54-5 143 327 332 335-6 339 343-4 408-9 412
	-all other plants	23 163 174-6 278-9 345-7 354 368-9 423-4 430 453
WHITE FRUIT	Trees	135 232 246-7 256 265 440-1
	Other Plants	55 146 321 410
WHITE UNDER LEAVES	Trees	8 12 107-8 111 201 212-3 216 234 265 271 386
	Other Plants	23 63 144 148 159 279 298 319 348 411 446
WHITE BARK/STEM	All Plants	7 8 12 45 87 91 93 110 190 278 282 308 378 397 435 451

○ Gold *I* Silver

GOLD/SILVER (On/under leaves) All Plants 57 100 115 144 197 217-8 277 309 311 377 478

● Black

BLACK FRUIT Trees	-fig or olive like 103 222 224 232-3 248
	-all other trees 32-3 42 105 117-8 130 203 210-1 213 215 239-41 249 261
	267-8 444 476
Other Plants	64 66 145 151 153 155 159 307 326 329 406 408
BLACK BARK/STEM	All Plants 43 51 283 292 443

The Keys

A KEY TO SOME PLANT TYPES

FERNS AND FERN ALLIES	25-27 82-84 183 286-300 302 420-1 454
GRASSES & SEDGES	75-7 79 168-73 358 360-1 424-5 447-8
PALMS -including Lawyer Vines	2-4 18 60-3 137-8 277-82
SUCCULENTS	28 72 74
TREE FERNS	283-5

VINES	-twining with tendrils	151 156 159 301 310 317 459
	-twining -no tendrils	64 68 157-8 160-2 306 309 311-2 318-9 321 324 326 414-5 419
	-scrambling	22 58 64-6 152-5 323 325 418 463 480
	-hooks or spines	2-4 67 280 306-7 313-4 416 477
	-clinging with roots	304 315-6 320 366 415

PARASITES/MISTLETOE	19-21 85-6 365 415
EPIPHYTES & ORCHIDS	23-4 28 82 84 163-7 286-8 290 300 322 368-9
LITHOPHYTES -on rocks	41 163 183 316 322 354 368-9
PLANTS THAT WINTER	9 39 53 102 116 118 232 244 253 333 398-9 438 470-1 473 476 484-5

A KEY TO TRUNK OR STEM CHARACTERISTICS

BARK PAPERY	44-6 120 260 378
BARK SMOOTH	8 11 14 87 91-3 113 185 190 237 275 373 378 397-9 435 476
BARK DEEPLY FISSURED	92 111 151 374 376 385 394
BARK FURROWED/FIBROUS	95 132 240 372 375 380-1 387 437
BARK FLAKING *(Not annual)*	8 9 186 193 275
FLOWERS/FRUIT ON TRUNK	200 223 225-6 228 251 383
STRANGLER/BANYAN	103-4 224 227 229-30 232-3

THORNY TRUNK/STEM -Trees	125 137-8 244 253 263
-Other Plants	2-4 67 141 143 150 280 303 306-7 313-4 336-7 416 460 467 477

TRUNKS WITH PROP ROOTS	5 6 10 16 446
BUTTRESS ROOTS	7 11-2 217 223 252 259 260 *(Partial list - this is a common attribute)*

The Keys

A KEY TO LEAF OR FOLIAGE CHARACTERISTICS

LEAVES LONG & NARROW	Trees	91 115 127 188-9 271 380-1 391 446
	Grasses/Sedges	75-81 168-73 184 360-4 447-8
	Other Plants	26-7 71 160 163 175-6 181 343 359 402 426-7
LEAVES LOBED (Finger-like)	Trees	125 194 197 237 271 273 397-9 476 478
	Other Plants	149-52 158 161 269 313 315 317 336 407 431 466
LEAVES WHORLED (Radiating)	Trees	32-3 40 121 202 205-6 227 229 244 270 384 386 435 444 469
	Other Plants	55 62 269-70 294 327-8 332 348-9 448-50
LEAVES HEART SHAPED		1 17 49 50 65 69 106-7 158 209 223 234 301 305 310-3 325 351-2
LEAVES NEEDLE LIKE		51 187 331 382 385 394-5 443
LEAVES SPIKY/STINGING		1 2-4 78-81 246 274 327 357 358
LEAVES IN THREES		213 217-8 236 254 325
LEAF TEXTURED/ROUGH		105 141 150 208 226 228 303-4 328-9 332 455 457-8
LEAF SERRATED/TOOTHED		1 121 128 130 147 216 239 246 261 263 265-6 268 272 283 291 303 314 344 356
FOLIAGE LAYERED		31-2 41 52 145 207 210 216 235 330
FOLIAGE WEEPING		45-6 131 133 188 400 436

A KEY TO SOME PLANT FAMILIES

EUCALYPTS/GUM TREES	87-96 190 373-8 481	PINES	185-9 275
WATTLES/ACACIAS	34-5 97-101 191-2	LILLY PILLIES	200 439-41
GROUND ORCHIDS	432-34 449	CYCADS	139 198 367
FIGS	103-5 223-33 383-4	GINGERS	177 345-7
PANDANUS	78 80-1 362-4 446	SOLANUMS	142-4 317 336-7
GREVILLEAS/HAKEAS	115 134 379-82 407 478	QUANDONGS	40 202-4

9

SOME HARMFUL PLANTS

1 Stinging Tree (Gympi Gympi)

While the forests of North Queensland are generally safe to explore, the Stinging Tree can inflict severe pain, and should be avoided. The fine silica hairs on leaves and stems act like small syringes, and continue to inject venom for several days. Sudden cooling of the site, even several months later, can produce a tingling sensation. The immediate pain is severe, and can cause swelling of the lymph glands. Rubbing the site makes things worse, leaving the points of the broken-off hairs embedded in the skin. There is **no** really effective treatment. Applying 'plastic skin' and then pulling it off does remove some of the hairs; Aboriginal people used the sticky sap from the roots to do this.

Dendrocnide moroides is a shrub or small tree that grows in areas in rainforest where extra light can penetrate. This means it is often found on roadsides and in clearings, or where a tree has fallen. The large leaves are heart shaped, and covered with fine stinging hairs. The edges are serrated, as though cut with pinking shears. The leaves sit horizontally (Above) on long stalks which may be pink or reddish in colour and are attached towards the centre of the leaf. The raspberry like fruits hang in clusters on the stem (Right).

Stinging Tree is found in rainforest from northern NSW to Iron Range in Cape York, extending north to Malaysia. It might be confused with Wild Raspberry (no 313) a thorny vine with lobed leaves, or Bleeding Heart (no 209) a tree with shiny heart shaped leaves. Look out for the large, hairy, heart-shaped leaves, with serrated edges, and avoid this dangerous plant.

Ht >4m   Lf >300x280mm   Fl Nov-Mar   Fr Feb-Oct   cluster>30mm

WARNING
Many native fruits in North Queensland are poisonous. Do not risk eating or tasting them, as even small amounts can be dangerous.

Harmful Plants

2 Wait-a-While

Calamus moti, or **Lawyer Vine,** is a rainforest vine that grows thin tendrils armed with sharp hooks. These can tear skin and clothing, and make walking through rainforest miserable where they are common. They cut, but do not sting. When caught, stop and back off, to release the hooks. Even the undersides of the leaves can carry hooks, but the top can be covered with fine upright hairs, pleasing to stroke. Wait-a-while grows large fronds with between 80 and 100 leaflets with finely spined edges. The small green or cream flowers (Right) have 3 petals, and are carried on what appears to be a modified tendril. The cream or yellow fruits resemble those of Hairy Mary (Bottom, Right).

All the Calamus species on this page are modified palms, and are amongst the world's longest plants. They provide the cane used for furniture, and once used for punishment in schools. Some start life as pleasant palm-like clumps, and only later produce the thorny stems which will eventually emerge in sunlight above the canopy. In rainforest one of the scarcest resources is light, and these plants have developed a successful strategy to get to it, despite having a slow start.

Ht 50m+ long   Lf >3mfrond, >600mmleaflets   Fl Jul-Aug 3-5mm   Fr Apr-Aug 8-14mm

3 Vicious Hairy Mary

Calamus radicalis is covered with the long sharp spines (Left) which give it its name. The larger spines are flat, and can produce a musical note if plucked. The fronds carry from 80 to 126 shiny leaflets and the flowers and fruits resemble those of the other species on this page. Vicious Hairy Mary can be found on Mt Whitfield in Cairns. The Rainforest Aborigines near Cairns called it 'bugul'.

Ht 50m+long   Lf >3mfrond, 300-600mmleaflets   Fl May-Jun 3-4mm   Fr Feb-Apr 8-10mm

4 Hairy Mary

Calamus australis can be recognised by the purple tint that often colours new fronds (Left). Although it resembles Wait-a-while (no 2) it has only 25-63 leaflets on a smaller frond. The stems are thickly covered with fine (>80mm) spines. The fruits (Right) are like intricately plaited small balls, hanging in bunches up to 2 metres long, and are eaten by Fruit Pigeons and Cassowaries. Aboriginal people had many uses for Calamus vines. They made a strong rope used for climbing trees and constructing the framework for shelters. They also made tough handles for axes and could be woven into eel and fish traps. The fine tendrils were used to lasso prawns.

These are native Queensland species. Another Calamus, Fishtail Lawyer Cane, is listed with rainforest palms (no 280). There are eight Calamus species in Australia, out of the 375 species known world wide.

Ht >50m+long   Lf 1-1.2mfrond,100-325mmleaf   Fl Feb-Jun   Fr Nov-Apr 10-17mm

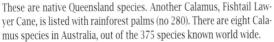

11

Mangroves comprise a group of trees (some botanists include other plants) that have adapted to the difficult and constantly changing conditions on the very edge of the sea. Most can tolerate salt water, either by excluding salt from the water they take in, or by exuding salt from their leaves. Since their roots are often immersed in water, they have evolved adaptations that allow air to reach their roots, either through buttresses or through special breathing roots that emerge from the mud into the air. Many mangroves produce fruits that develop into young plants before falling from the tree.

Once despised as mosquito ridden swamps, mangroves are now protected in Queensland, and they are increasingly valued as a rich source of nutrients for fish and other wildlife. The easiest way to appreciate the unique smells, sounds and sights of the mangroves is from a boardwalk. Excellent boardwalks are located close to the airport in Cairns, and on the way to Cape Tribulation. Mangroves also line many of the major drains in Cairns, and can be seen at Centenary Lakes. And though mangroves have no more mosquitoes and sand flies than other swampy areas, take some repellant along, just in case.

5 Red Mangrove

Rhizophora stylosa is possibly the best known mangrove in Queensland (Right). The trees grow close to the water, their roots becoming submerged at high tide. Some of the looping roots act as breathing roots, getting air to the otherwise submerged root system. Sometimes roots descend from the branches. The rough bark is grey to dark brown. This mangrove excludes salt from the water it takes in.

The leaves are large and often have a small spike on the tip. They cluster at the ends of the branches, and are a lighter green underneath, but speckled with tiny brown spots. The flowers are small and white. The fruits, already a small plant, taper to a point. The fruit is actually the top 'knob', and the spear below can be green to purplish. Fruit can be found all year. Break a fruit, and the broken surface is furry to touch with hundreds of fine silica hairs. Red Mangroves are found from northern NSW across tropical Australia and into SE Asia and the Pacific. The hard red timber is used overseas for construction and for tanning nets.

Ht >20m   Lf 45-150mm   Fl Feb-May 8-13mm   Fr Any month 15-50mm spear 200-650mm

Mangroves

6 Tall Stilted Mangrove

Rhizophora apiculata is very similar to the Red Mangrove (no 5) but the shiny leaves are more pointed and lack the brown speckles underneath. The trees grow in dense stands close to the seaward margin of the mangroves. The flowers have 'woolly' petals and the fruits are similar to the Red Mangrove, though longer (>600mm). The photo shows how the fruit can separate from the long spear root to which it is attached. Tall Stilted Mangroves grow between Rockhampton and the Torres Strait, and across SE Asia and the Pacific Islands. The wood is difficult to work, but is good for firewood and charcoal. Young shoots have been eaten in Singapore, and produce medicines to assist digestion and control bleeding.

Ht >25m Lf 80-190mm Fl Apr&Aug 8-11mm Fr Aug-Oct

7 Yellow Mangrove

Ceriops tagal often forms a distinct zone within the mangroves, surrounding open salt pans or along small tidal channels away from the sea. The trees are small with buttress-like roots and sometimes with stilts and breather roots. Their leaves are yellowish, erect and fleshy. The growing point is distinctive, shaped like a lance head, while the leaves grow in opposite pairs. The upward pointing bunches of smallish leaves reduce vulnerability to strong sunlight, and the small orange flowers can be found hanging below them, with viviparous fruit following. Yellow Mangrove grows across northern Australia and the Indo-Pacific area. It produces dyes used in batik printing, and the tough, durable timber is suitable for tool handles and pit props, although mangroves are protected in Qld. The shoots provided an anti-malarial medicine.

Ht >15m Lf 30-100mm Fl Jan-Nov 2-4mm Fr May-Jan 15-28mm

8 Grey Mangrove

Avicennia marina, the Grey Mangrove, is easily seen when the wind blows, revealing the grey-white underside of the leaves. The bark ranges in colour from grey-white to green and is smooth, sometimes flaky. The Grey Mangrove is a small tree and is found throughout the mangrove habitat from the sea to the land. The leaves in less salty environments are longer and lancelike, while those in very saline areas may be small, leathery and rounded. The leaves secrete salt from special glands on the whitish underside. Lick the underside of the leaf to taste the salt. The roots are about the thickness of a pencil and are peg-like above ground. The small pale-orange flowers are followed by green, almond-like, velvety fruit. The Grey Mangrove is hardy, tolerating colder climates (it is found in Victoria) and fresher water than many other species. It occurs from Africa to Japan and the Western Pacific. It can absorb heavy metal pollution, but is easily destroyed by oil, which clogs its breathing roots. It is common in Cairns city in the drains.

Ht >16m Lf 30-115mm Fl Oct-Mar 5-6mm Fr Jan-May 20-30mm

9 Cedar Mangrove

Xylocarpus moluccensis (prev. X. mekongensis) is a mangrove which is readily identified by its robust upright breathing roots. The tree grows with a rough flaking bark that persists, making it an ideal host for many epiphytes. The leaves are compound, with from 2 to 8 leaflets arranged in pairs along a leaf stalk. The flowers are small, white or pink, and are fragrant. The fruits are as large as an apple, ripening to brown, and containing several large seeds. The breathing roots can be seen (Right) near some crab holes in the mud. Crabs rapidly remove fallen leaves.

Cedar Mangrove grows from Central Queensland to Cape York and across the north of Australia. It is native to Africa and the Indo-Pacific area, so is a widely distributed tree. It is related to Australia's premium cabinet timber, the Red Cedar (no 193) and has an attractive red cedar-like timber, though more inclined to split. Like Red Cedar, it 'winters' each year (about Sep-Oct) losing all its leaves and quickly growing a new crop. It is easily identified prior to wintering as its leaves turn yellow and orange before falling (Above). Cedar Mangrove is scattered through the other mangroves at the Cairns Airport boardwalks, mostly near salt water creeks.

Ht >30m   Lf 35-170mm   Fl Sep-Oct 3-5mm   Fr Dec-Feb 45-110mm

10 Large-fruited Orange Mangrove

Bruguiera gymnorhiza, the Large-fruited Orange Mangrove, is one of five Brugiera species growing in Far North Queensland. All produce knee-like breathing roots (Below) although they can also develop prop roots. They grow into medium to large trees with large smooth leaves with whitish stalks. The underside of the leaves may be reddish and dotted black. Another common name for this tree is the **Large Leaved Mangrove**. The fruit (Right) is an orange to red frilled berry capping a long pointed spear, which can penetrate the mud.

Large-fruited Orange Mangrove is found from Grafton in NSW to Cape York and the NT. It grows from Africa through the Indo-Pacific area. In Singapore the leaves and peeled seedlings were eaten, and the timber was used for poles and pilings. In Indonesia it is planted for woodchip production. The bark provides a red-brown dye, as well as a medicine for malaria, and even an adhesive. Scent was produced from the roots, and the leaves produce a medicine for blood pressure control.

Mangrove roots penetrate as deep as 2 metres into the mud. One teaspoon full of mangrove mud can contain 10 billion bacteria, making it an incredibly rich food source for fish and crustaceans. Mangroves are believed to have originated near Far North Queensland, leading to the great diversity of species found here today.

Ht >36m   Lf 45-220mm   Fl Oct-Jul 13-16mm long   Fr Dec 15-45mm berry, 120-250mm spear

Mangroves

11 Cannonball Mangrove

Xylocarpus granatum grows a fruit that clearly suggests its common name. The tree can grow buttresses and ribbon like roots. The smooth bark is usually a light yellowish or greenish colour, with pink-orange blotches, commonly with interesting knobs and protrusions. Like the Cedar Mangrove (no 9) it is closely related to Australia's premium cabinet timber, Red Cedar (no 193) and it too is a deciduous tree. The leaves are compound, comprised of 2-6 rounded leaflets, bright light green when new, darkening with age. When ripe the fruits explode, producing intricately shaped segments which are a puzzle to put together again. These segments are common on local beaches. Cannonball Mangroves occur from Cape York to Fraser Island, and can be seen from the Marrdja boardwalk, close to the edge of Noah Creek. They are generally found some distance from the salt water, and even in neighbouring rainforest. While the timber is used in East Africa and Asia for carpentry, boat-building and high quality wood carvings, in Queensland mangroves are protected and not logged. The timber is supposed to repel ants, and the bark produces an umber dye.

Ht >25m   Lf 40-150mm   Fl Oct-Jan 4-5mm   Fr Jan-Sep 75-200mm

12 Looking-glass Mangrove

Heritiera littoralis is a common mangrove near Cape Tribulation, accessible from boardwalks in that area. It is most likely to be noticed for its sinuous ribbon like buttress roots. The tree grows with a pale, smooth to flaking bark, and large, untidy leaves which are dark green above and pale beneath. The tree often has an open and somewhat bedraggled canopy. The flowers lack petals, but the sepals are green outside and red or purple inside with the unusual keeled nuts following. The nuts hang in clusters from the branches or can be found on the mud below the trees. The Looking-glass Mangrove, found from Cape York to Mackay, prefers the less saline environment on the landward side of the mangroves. It is one of the tallest of the mangroves, and in South East Asia the best trunks were used for boat masts or telegraph poles, the timber being hard and strong. In Africa the main use was for firewood, and especially for making charcoal, where logs are covered with earth and burnt in a slow fire for several days. The wood has also been used for building, furniture construction and carving. The nuts have been used to treat diarrhoea and dysentery, and have also been used for adulterating the drink Cola, though they do not have its properties.

Ht >15m   Lf 140-290mm   Fl Mar-Apr 5-7mm   Fr Apr-Nov 50-100mm

15

13 Wrinkle Pod Mangrove

Cynometra iripa, the Wrinkle Pod Mangrove, is named for its unusual looking fruits (Above, Left) which somewhat resemble a lobe from a brain, with a beak attached. The small pink or cream flowers produce fruit only in wet years. The trees above were photographed on the banks of Keatings Lagoon, near Cooktown, where they grow under shade near fresh water, as is their habit. They occur near sea level in both rainforest and mangrove habitats, usually as small trees, from Cape York to Mackay, the NT, and through SE Asia to India.

Ht >8m Lf 15-100mm Fl May-Oct Fr Sep-Jun 25-48mm

14 River Mangrove

Aegicerus corniculatum has rounded leaves which exude salt; often appearing wet from absorbed moisture. It is a small tree with smooth grey bark that is found near Port Douglas colonizing sandflats. The flowers are in groups of 15-20, white, and variously described as 'fragrant' or 'smelling of rotten bananas'. The fruits resemble curved bean pods with a spike on the end. River Mangroves prefer less saline river edges, growing from Jervis Bay in NSW through North Queensland, as far north as China. The bark is a fish poison, yet the leaves are edible. This is one of only two species of Aegicerus worldwide.

Ht >7m Lf 25-100mm Fl May-Nov 5-11mm Fr Mar-Apr 20-80mm

15 White Flowered Black Mangrove

Lumnitzera racemosa lacks breathing roots (pneumatophores) and is found on the landward side of the mangroves. At the boardwalks near the Cairns Airport, this small tree grows alongside the airport road, and provides a massed display of fragrant white flowers. The Mangrove Clerodendrum (no 22) enjoys the same conditions and can be found scrambling through these mangroves. Flowers are followed by the fruit, a green nut. The leaves have a small gland near the apex on the underside, and the point is slightly indented.

This is one of two Lumnitzera mangroves to be found in Queensland, extending along the whole of the east coast, and also found in S.E. Asia, the Pacific Islands and Africa. The other (no 16) has red flowers on a similar but smaller tree. There is also a pink flowered hybrid. The leaves are reported as having been eaten during famine, and the wood is useful for firewood. The bark can be used for tanning and recent research in India has discovered a new aromatic ester in the wood.

Ht >10m Lf 20-97mm Fl Jul-May 4-5mm Fr Nov-Feb 9-15mm

Mangroves

16 Red Flowered Black Mangrove

Lumnitzera littorea is a small mangrove which grows bright red flowers. Knee shaped breathing roots may be attached to the roots. The fragrant flowers are followed by corky capsule-like nuts (>15mm) each containing a single seed. The fleshy leaves with a small gland on the underside near the apex, are held upright on short stems.

Red Flowered Black Mangroves are widely spread from East Africa, through SE Asia to Australia and Polynesia. In Australia they are found from Cape York to Hinchinbrook Island, and in the NT. These plants were seen at the mouth of the Daintree River. The plants have some ornamental potential, and in Asia, where they grow much larger, the trunks were used for firewood and timber. Aboriginal people sucked the nectar and used the wood for digging and throwing sticks.

Ht >10m Lf 20-80mm Fl any month 10-20mm Fr May-Aug

17 Club Mangrove

Aegialitis annulata is an untidy shrub with a trunk swollen at the base, but no above ground roots. The shiny heart shaped leaves are on long stems that wrap around the stalk. These leaves can secrete considerable quantities of salt (see photo at Right) and it is possible that the salt secreting glands are precursors of the sticky glands used by related plants to trap insects. The shrubs, with dark deeply cracked bark, are usually found next to salt marsh or on rocks near the seaward side of the mangroves. The white flowers are pollinated by ants, and are followed by thin red-brown cylindrical fruit. The Club mangrove is found from Cape York to Fraser Island, and in the NT, extending into SE Asia. It is one of only 2 species of Aegialitis worldwide.

Ht >4m Lf 30-80mm Fl Oct-Feb 8-10mm Fr Feb 45-50mm

18 Nypa Palm

Nypa fruticans is a palm that grows in brackish water and is generally regarded as a mangrove. It is also called **Mangrove Palm**. This is a clumping palm with underground stems and long compound leaves composed of dark green leaflets which are whitish underneath. The 3-petalled flowers are yellow or purple, and are followed by large pandanus like fruits consisting of numerous reddish-brown or black woody nuts clustered together. There is one white seed per segment. Nypa Palm occurs between Cape York and the Herbert River, and also in the NT, through PNG and SE Asia into India. 70m year old fossil pollen has been found, even in London, showing it once had a 'tropical' climate. The sap can be tapped for a drink, sugar, toddy or vinegar, and the fruit's flesh is edible.

Ht >13m Lf 4-10m frond, 600-1500mm Fl Nov-Dec Fr any month 300-500mm head, 100-150mm

Mangrove Mistletoes

19 Mistletoe

Amyema queenslandicum is a broad leaved mistletoe which is parasitic on many plants. Parasites attach themselves to a host plant and feed off it, unlike epiphytes which simply use their host for support. It is found from Coen to Ingham and in PNG. This was growing on a Cedar Mangrove (no 9) adjacent to the western boardwalk near the Cairns Airport. The leaf of this mistletoe does not match the leaves of the host tree, which are visible at the bottom of the photograph, as is the case with some mistletoes. Indeed, the parasite forms a distinct bunch of vegetation which is clearly different to the host. The leaves are rounded, thick and leathery, with three to five vague veins radiating from the base. The flowers are orange or red. Like many mistletoes the fruit is sticky and is spread by the Mistletoe Bird, which has a habit of wiping the sticky seeds onto branches, where they are ideally placed to start a new plant. The male Mistletoe Bird has bright red patches under its throat and tail, with a glossy black back, so is quite a striking small bird. Mistletoe Birds are found throughout Australia wherever mistletoe grows.

Ht >2m   Lf 40-80mm   Fl Mar-Dec 30-35mm   Fr Jun-Dec 8-10mm

20 Mistletoe

Amyema glabrum is another mistletoe found growing on mangroves, with conspicuous smooth leaves which are yellowish in colour. The fleshy leaves are either without stalks or the stems are very short. The flowers can be green, yellow or cream, possibly with a red base. The fruits (Left) are small berries and are green to yellow, containing a single seed surrounded by sticky flesh. The green seed is attached to a long hair-like tail that protrudes from the fruit. The fruits grow in groups of three, the middle fruit with no stem, and the fruits on either side on short stalks.

This species of mistletoe occurs in rainforest and mangroves, from Bloomfield River to Mission Beach.

Ht >2m+   Lf 18-80mm   Fl Mar-Oct 22-30mm   Fr Aug-Oct 8mm

21 Mistletoe

Viscum articulatum is a mistletoe that lives on mistletoe! As can be seen from the photograph below, the Viscum mistletoe hangs from a broadleaved mistletoe (probably an Anyema, like those above) which is hanging from a mangrove tree. It would be possible to find these mistletoes attached to a tree such as the Mistletoe Tree (see no 112) that is itself a root parasite.

This aerial shrub grows to about one metre across, with flattened stems in segments about 10-45mm long. The actual leaves are  tiny, as are the orange flowers, which occur at any time of year. The fruits are yellow to pale pink berries containing one tailed seed. This mistletoe occurs in open forest as well as mangroves between Cape York and Glenbrook in NSW. It also occurs in WA and the NT, and through Asia and the Pacific.

Lf .5mm, stems 10-45mm   Fl any month   Fr Feb-Oct 3-6mm

Mangrove Associates

22 Mangrove Clerodendrum

Clerodendrum inerme is a scrambling vine or shrub. The elongated flowers are white, sometimes with a touch of purple, and with reddish stamens. They occur in any month, and are fragrant. The fruit is a smallish four seeded nut, dark brown in colour. The leaf stalks are often purple. These vines were adjacent to the Cairns airport road near the boardwalks and were flowering in Feb. They prefer the landward side of the mangroves. Two systemic anti-viral proteins have been discovered in this plant and Hiroshima University has identified three new compounds from its leaves. Somewhat surprisingly, it is also starring as an attractive bonsai plant.

Ht >6m Lf 30-120mm Fl 15-40mm Fr Mar-Dec 10-20mm

23 Button Orchid

Dischidia nummularia, despite its common name, is not an orchid at all. It is found in trees such as paperbarks which offer light shade, often with orchids such as the Teatree Orchid growing in the same tree. The leaves are thick and succulent, carried on thin stems that produce a milky sap. The photograph at left shows two plants with different coloured leaves. The white, rather mealy looking form is commonly seen near Cooktown, while the green form is more common near Cairns. The flowers (Right) are small and white. There are three other related species in the area. A good place to see these plants is on the Esplanade in Cairns, where it grows on a tree almost opposite the night markets.

Lf 6-15mm Fl any month 2-3mm Fr any month 25-40mm

24 Ant Plant (Butterfly Plant)

This strange plant is common in mangroves, but grows more widely in coastal areas. *Myrmecodia beccarii* is the species found near Cairns, with another four species seen only in Cape York. They were first collected by Joseph Banks in 1770. The tuber is a mass of tunnels; smooth walled tunnels inhabited by tiny ants, and rough walled tunnels that the ants use as toilets and the plant uses as an intestine to gather nutrients from the ants' waste. So the ants help feed the plant and if disturbed will protect the colony and the plant. But even stranger, the Apollo Jewel butterfly lays its eggs on the ant plant. The ants take in the baby caterpillars and care for them as they eat the fleshy tuber and guard them when they go out at night to eat the leaves. In return the caterpillars secrete a sugary liquid to feed the ants. The caterpillars cut an escape hole before pupating and fly off quickly once they emerge as adults.

Ht >500mm Lf 60-120mm Fl Nov-Feb >20mm Fr Nov-Feb 10mm

Mangrove Ferns

25 Mangrove Fern

Acrostichum speciosum is a fern that can tolerate salt water and so is often found growing amongst mangroves. Two of the world's three species of Acrosticum are found in Australia, this being the smaller, more salt-tolerant one. Mangrove Fern can grow to about 2 metres, with upright, pinnate (branching once) fronds. The narrow ends to the lower fronds is distinctive. Like all Acrostichums, some of the upper leaves are fertile, and the whole undersurface of each leaf is covered with brown sporangia, bearing the spores which are the fern's equivalent of seeds. Ferns evolved before seed bearing plants.

Mangrove Fern is found from Cape York to northern NSW, the NT and WA, and across tropical Asia. It forms large clumps in mangroves and river estuaries. Aboriginal people ate the roasted rhizomes.

26 Tape Fern (Primitive Plant)

Vittaria elongata is a fern with long narrow fronds, without any branching. This is one of two species of Vittaria identified in Australia. They are very similar in appearance and habitat, often growing from the base of a Basket Fern (no 286) like the one pictured here near the Marrdja boardwalk. The other species (*Vittaria ensiformis*) has shorter rhizomes and longer, somewhat thinner leaves. Tape Fern has also been called the '**Stiff Shoestring Fern**', and grows best near to the sea.

Tape Fern is very widely spread, occurring across the Pacific in Hawaii, Easter Island and Pitcairn, and through S.E. Asia to Taiwan and west to Sri Lanka and Zimbabwe. In Ceylon it was believed that a paste made from the leaves would promote hair growth, and women would wrap this paste in fabric around their heads at night.

This is a slow growing fern that is hard to establish as a garden plant.

27 Skeleton Fork Fern (Primitive Plant)

Psilotum nudum is a finely branching fern-like plant found as an epiphyte in mangroves. It is one of two Fork-ferns in North Queensland. In Southern Australia it grows upright from rock crevices, but here it often hangs down as an epiphyte. The spores are held in the yellow three-lobed structures towards the ends of the

branches (>600mm). The specimens shown here were near the Marrdja boardwalk. The other Fork Fern has flattened stems.

These ancient plants dominated the Carboniferous era, about 300 million years ago, and are not true ferns, but the simplest surviving vascular plants. In Japan they have been valued and collected for more than 400 years, with the rarest of the 300 forms fetching very high prices.

Mangrove Orchid

28 Golden Orchid

Durabaculum undulatum (Prev. Dendrobium discolor) is still found in mangroves and forest close to the coast, but in smaller numbers than in the past due to excessive collecting. The beautiful sprays of flowers can be over a metre long, ranging from clear yellow to chocolate brown, and they have become the basis for many hybrid forms produced by orchid fanciers. This orchid can grow on rocks subjected to salt spray from the sea, as well as in sheltered areas such as those (Below) which were well inland from the waves. The stems can exceed 2 metres in length (Left), with leaves alternating along the ribbed stem. The Golden Orchid is Australia's largest orchid. It is also found in PNG.

About 900 species of Dendrobium occurred in Asia, Australia and the Pacific Islands, though the genus has now been extensively reorganised. Many carry their flowers on graceful sprays such as these. Most flowers are borne in spring.

29 Samphire

Samphires are a group of plants, including species of *Halosarcia* (Below), which grow on saltpans amongst mangroves. The succulent stems can store water in special tissues for use in dry periods, but the plants are also resistant to occasional inundation by salt water. Exposed to wind and sun, it is hard to imagine a more difficult situation in which to survive. These tough plants have no real leaves, but the swollen stems, which often have pink, red or purple coloration, also perform the functions of leaves. The samphire below is near to the boardwalks at Cairns airport.

SHORE & SWAMP

In this section the focus is on those plants which are found along the coast either close to the beach or in the swamps which often lie close behind it. Cairns itself is built on low-lying ground, where peak tides still bring salt water up the gutters in Sheridan Street to the front of the Courthouse. The Cairns Central Swamp is home to large numbers of Giant Fruit Bats, or Flying Foxes, and between Centenary Lakes and the Botanic Gardens in Collins Street a boardwalk provides easy access to this swamp environment. Though much of the North Queensland coast is mangrove fringed, there are also many miles of beaches and headlands. Sadly, residential development continues to eat away at the remaining coastal plant communities, in spite of attempts to better manage this threatened ecosystem.

30 Beach Calophyllum

Calophyllum inophyllum grows into a large tree, commonly found overhanging the beach, like the tree below at Cape Tribulation. The short trunk supports large sprawling branches. The closely spaced parallel veins in the leaf (Lower Right) run from the midrib to the edge, uninterrupted. Flowers are white, with a yellow centre. The seeds are spherical, about the size of a golf ball, and float large distances on the ocean. They are common in flotsam on the beach (Right). Beach Callophyllum wood is densely interwoven, making the timber extremely strong and resistant to splitting. It was often used for boat knees. However, if the timber is sawn thin enough, internal stresses in the wood may tear it apart.

Ht >30m   Lf 80-200mm   Fl Dec-Feb&Jun 9-16mm   Fr Feb-Oct 25-50mm

31 Beach Almond

Terminalia catappa is a handsome tree with layered branches of rather untidy large leaves. The small flowers are white or yellow, in spikes on the ends of the branches, and the fruit is a pinkish, fading to fawn, fibrous nut with a small edible kernal; the 'almond'. It makes a good shade tree, but is briefly deciduous, losing its leaves in order to 'winter' (Above).

Beach Almond occurs from Cape York to Proserpine, but originated in India, and is also known as the **Indian Almond** or **Sea Almond**, and there are numerous other names in use around the world. In Taiwan the fallen leaves were used to produce a drug for treating liver diseases. The plant has anticarcinogenic potential, with antioxidant properties. Tea made from the leaves was used to treat dysentery and diarrhoea. The kernals have some value as an aphrodisiac, and fish breeders use the plant to keep certain tropical fish healthy. Although the kernal is small, it is widely eaten, and improved varieties with softer shells and larger kernals have potential as an edible crop.

Ht >16m+   Lf 100-330mm   Fl Oct-May 10-26mm   Fr Feb-Apr 50-80mm

Steve Hurst @ USDA-NRCS Plants Database

32 Brown Damson

Terminalia arenicola is a second Terminalia species found on beaches in Far North Queensland. It is quite similar to the Beach Almond (Above) but with slightly smaller leaves and a less layered appearance. Trees grow to about 11m in height.

The fruits, while similar, are much smaller and when ripe are purple-black to violet-red, elongated and fleshy, with a hard stone (Left). The flowers are borne in spikes above the branches, and have an unpleasant scent, while the fruits occur throughout the year. These are eaten by Cassowaries. Brown Damson trees are found from Cape York to Caloundra in SE Queensland, up to about 40m above sea level. There are 24 species of Terminalia in Australia, some of which are inland trees, but the two on this page are truly beach plants.

Ht >11m   Lf 100-200mm   Fl Sep-May 5-7mm   Fr any month 25-40mm

33 Mueller's Damson (Butterfly Plant)

Terminalia muelleri is a rather untidy smaller Damson that is similar to the two previous Terminalia trees, but more open, and not so layered. The branches don't droop, and they resist breakage. The leathery leaves are similar in appearance to the other Terminalia species, in untidy whorls on the end of the branches, but they tend to be smaller, and often look bedraggled. They may be hairy on the underside, where two flat glands are located near the base. The white flowers occur in a cluster of spikes radiating from within the leaves. They can occur at any time of year. The fruits are blue, purple or black. They are considered edible, and are eaten by many species of birds. The photograph comes from near the Rex Lookout on the Cook Highway between Cairns and Port Douglas. Mueller's Damson, also known as '**Jam Fruit**' in Cape York, is often referred to overseas, where it is grown as an ornamental tree, as '**Australian Almond**'. It occurs between Cape York and Rockhampton (>150m altitude). Mueller's Damson contains ellagic acid, and has high antioxidant activity. It is a host plant for species of *Arhopela* butterfly.

Ht >18m Lf 50-150mm Fl any month 3-5mm Fr Jan-May 12-20mm

34 Coastal Wattle

Acacia oraria is a wattle that grows right on the beach, where it offers some dense shade. The tree has whitish angled stems, bearing rounded soft leaves that are actually phyllodes, or flattened stems, with short leaf stalks. The fragrant flowers are white to creamy yellow. The twisted pods change from purple-green to a whitish brown, and hold a number of black seeds wrapped around with an aril (supposedly red on the coast - orange inland) and tightly constricted within the pods. (Photo, Left)

Coastal Wattle occurs between Cape York and Carmila south of Mackay, and in Timor. It mostly grows on sand on the coast, but occurs inland north of Cairns on streams. It has been used to control Blady Grass, the worst weed of SE Asia.

Ht >10m Lf 50-125mm Fl Feb-Sep 5-8mm Fr Sep-Oct 40-140mm

35 Lancewood

Acacia crassicarpa is an upright tree bearing large oval pods. Its other common name of **Northern Golden Wattle** refers to the cream to yellow-gold flower spikes (Right). The leaves are large and usually strongly curved, often rather yellow in appearance and with a gland at the base. Lancewood occurs from Cape York to Mackay, and also in PNG. Since seed collection began in PNG about 1980, it has risen to become one of the three most important Acacias in SE Asia, with large plantations in Sumatra feeding pulp mills. While trees grow 25m in 7 years, there have been social and environmental costs due to the huge monocultures of this tree in Indonesia, even though it does successfully control Blady Grass, a major weed in the area.

Ht >30m Lf 80-270mm Fl Apr-Sep 4-8mm Fr Aug-Nov 30-120

36 Red Beech

Dillenia alata is one of the most striking trees of the coastal swamps, but it is also found throughout coastal areas, including hilltops some distance from the sea. The bright yellow flowers (Right) are borne throughout the year, but last only one day, and are followed by reddish capsules containing the seeds. Aboriginal people reportedly ate both the flower petals and the white arils surrounding the fruit. It is, though, the unusual red flaky bark (copper/pink to maroon) that is most likely to attract attention (Left). These trees seem to glow in the dark swampy environments where they thrive. Some trees, for example street trees on the Esplanade in Cairns, do not show this bark colour. Another common name for this tree is the **Golden Guinea Tree**. There are 60 species of Dillenia in Asia, but only this one in Australia. '*Alata*' means winged, and refers to the winged leaf stalks.

Ht >15m   Lf 110-230mm   Fl 80mm   Fr Aug-Feb

37 Red Coondoo

Mimusops elengi is a little known native tree with an amazing range of uses. The tree has distinctive grey tesselated bark, and can be found on the beaches north of Cairns. The cream or white flowers are fragrant, and occur throughout the year. The fruits ripen from yellow to orange to red and contain one or two forked brown seeds. In Asia the fruits are eaten, and the trees are sometimes large enough to mill. The fallen flowers retain their attractive scent for several days, and are offered at shrines or used in garlands woven into hair. The oil is now extracted for perfumes. One of the ayurvedic medicinal plants, it was used for a multitude of medicinal purposes; treating snake-bite, tooth ache, and as a contraceptive. It is now known to have anti-HIV and anti-fungal properties. Some 74 compounds have been isolated from the flowers alone. It produces dyes superior to synthetic products and is used in bonsai.

Ht >16m   Lf 40-140mm   Fl Any month
12-16mm   Fr Apr-Dec 12-18mm

38 Mango Pine

Barringtonia calyptrata in full bloom can be quite spectacular, with masses of greenish yellow flowers amongst the bright green new foliage. It is one of four freshwater mangroves growing in North Queensland, usually beside fresh water near the coast. The tree is deciduous, and the flowers, pendulous spikes growing

off the mature branches, appear along with the new leaves. Mango Pine occurs from Ingham to Cape York (also PNG) and can be found on the Esplanade in Cairns. The green or blue fruit is eaten by Cassowaries. The timber is soft and white, like pine, and the fruits smell of mangoes. It is also known as 'Corned-beef Wood Tree', from the smell of the wood.

*Ht >30m   Lf 150-390mm   Fl Jul-Feb
Fr Dec-Jan 50-95mm*

39 Freshwater Mangrove

Barringtonia acutangula is found along the margins of waterways where its long trailing flower spikes are instantly recognisable. The tree may be deciduous, losing its long leaves in the dry season. The flowers are pink to red with a green calyx, and occur in any month. The ribbed fruits occur from Jan to May, and are often found in flotsam on beaches. Freshwater mangroves are found from Cape York to Hinchinbrook Island, as well as in the NT, WA, and through SE Asia to India. Aboriginal people used the plant as a fish poison, and also produced an analgesic from it. The seeds contain saponins, and an antimicrobial agent is made from the bark. Some people believe its oil 'heals' mental prejudice!

Ht >25m   Lf 50-230mm   Fl 12-20mm   Fr Jan-may 20-60mm

40 Blue Quandong

Elaeocarpus grandis, also known as the **Silver Quandong**, is a handsome straight tree with distinctively radiating branches, angled upwards from the trunk at about 45 degrees (Right). The peach like leaves are borne in radiating 'hands' on the ends of the branches. This, and the presence of occasional orange or red leaves amongst the green is typical of many of the two dozen species of Elaeocarpus found in the rainforest. Blue Quandong is found from Cape York to NSW, often in swamps, but

also high up nearby mountains. The fruit is one of the most distinctive in the rainforest, with its blue or purple metallic lustre. They are a favourite food of the Wompoo Pigeon. The pitted stones were once used as counters in the board game of Chinese Checkers. The timber is of good quality and it is grown in plantations.

Ht >35m   Lf 80-150mm   Fl Oct-Mar   Fr 15-33mm

Shore & Swamp - Trees

41 Umbrella Tree

Schefflera actinophylla has been included here as it is often found on the coast, but it also grows in rainforest and open forest throughout the region, and quite often is found as an epiphyte growing in another tree, or on rocks. The large and shiny umbrella like clusters of leaves have made this Queensland native a popular indoor plant world wide.

The bright red spikes of rather crude flowers and fruit are attractive to many birds and animals which feed on them. Musky Rat Kangaroos, Red-legged Pademelons, and Spectacled Flying Foxes are included in the list of those which are attracted to the fruit. The main stem may carry several branches, each with its rosettes of dark leaves, but the wood is soft and trees rarely exceed 15 metres.

Ht >24m   Lf 80-300mm   Fl Aug-Mar 5-7mm   Fr Oct-May 6-8mm

42 Red Ash

Alphitonia excelsa bears dark green leaves with very white undersides. If rubbed in water they produce a soapy froth, hence its other common name, **Soap Bush**. Red Ash grows in a wide range of soils and situations, often as a small tree or shrub. Here (Right) it shows thin, dry season foliage just behind the coastal sand dunes at Palm Cove. The flowers are greenish-white and the fruits turn from green to black, falling away to leave only the orange to red seeds, eaten by some birds. Aboriginal people used the froth from this leaf to poison fish. The stunned fish would float to the surface of the pool where they were easily captured. Red Ash occurs from Cape York to northern NSW, and in PNG.

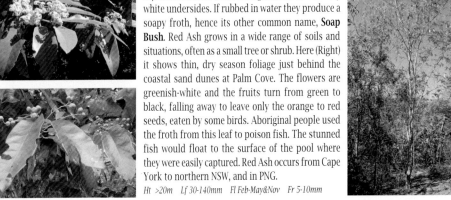

Ht >20m   Lf 30-140mm   Fl Feb-May&Nov   Fr 5-10mm

43 Australian Ebony

Diospyros compacta (Right) is one of about 20 species of this family found in Australia. The name Diospyros means 'divine fruit', and the family includes Ebony and Persimmon. The black timber known as Ebony comes from an overseas species. While most local Diaspyros live on the coast, they extend inland as well. The colourful fruits often have a large calyx, with three lobes, where the fruit is attached to its stem. This particular species grows right on the beach where the tree may be shaped by the wind. It has a very dark, almost black, trunk. There are separate male and female plants. Small yellow flowers with 3 petals are followed by the yellow, orange or red fruit. Fruit Doves enjoy the fruit. Australian Ebony occurs across tropical Australia, extending from Cape York to Shoalwater Bay in SE Qld.

Ht >11m   Lf 20-100mm   Fl Sep-Nov   Fr Dec-Apr 6-13mm

44 Broad Leaved Paperbark

Melaleuca viridiflora is a paperbark which can grow on dry areas such as a rocky headland (Below) as well as in swamps with its roots submerged for long periods of time. It differs from most other *Melaleuca* species in the width of its leaves, which are broad, oval, flat and stiff. Like all this family, though, its bark is thin and papery, in layers that separate readily. The bark is believed to protect against fire by insulating the tree, even if the outside burns. This tree grows greenish-cream flowers (Right) that give it its name, but it can also produce pink to red flowering forms (Below). The seed capsules are visible on the stem (Right). It is a source of Naiouli Oil, which is used to treat skin infections, being a strongly antibiotic oil, as well as preventing skin burns from radiation therapy. Along with the Weeping Paperbark (Below), the Broad Leaved Paperbark is host to a rare association between nematodes and flies that produce galls in new growth. Each species of fly is usually associated with only one species of Paperbark.

Ht >20m   Lf 55-220x10-60mm   Fl any month 14-25mm filaments   Fr any month 3-6mm

45 Weeping Paperbark

Melaleuca leucadendra is another common coastal tree, growing to a large size in swampy areas. The photograph (Right) shows a young tree with characteristic flaking bark and weeping foliage. Below is a photograph of an older tree in bloom. The masses of flowers attract Rainbow Lorikeets and other birds during the day, and Flying Foxes at night. The flowers are strongly scented; some say of caramel, others suggest mashed potato. Like mangroves, these trees have adapted to prolonged flooding of their roots by producing fibrous breathing roots, which shrivel and disappear in the dry season. The dense root systems make them the tree of choice for river bank stabilisation. Aboriginal people used the bark for roofing, cooking and even to construct coffins for funerals.

Ht >40m   Lf 55-230mm   Fl any month 7-25mm filaments   Fr any month 3-4mm

46 Grey Paperbark

Melaleuca dealbata is a paperbark which grows in seasonally wet areas in rainforest and open forest, particularly on old dune areas behind the beach and on riverbanks, waterholes and swamps. The bark is rougher than the similar Weeping Paperbark, and often coloured brown or grey. The foliage is blue-grey and is pendulous. Grey Paperbark is a slow growing tree found from Cape York to Maryborough, and also in the NT, WA, and through PNG into Indonesia. The wood is hard and suitable for construction, and the flowers provide good nectar for honey production. The tree is used for shelter belts and erosion control, as well as bauxite mine restoration. Also known as **Cloudy Teatree**.

Ht >25m   Lf 42-130mm   Fl Jul-Jan   Fr May-Dec 2-4mm

47 Paperbark Ti-tree

Melaleuca foliolosa is a small tree shown here growing near mangroves on the banks of the Annan River near Cooktown. It is also known as 'Scale-leaved Ti-tree' or just as 'Melaleuca'. What immediately attracts attention is the very small size of the leaves, which are indeed scale-like, yet the tree is quite dense and offers better

shade than most of its neighbours. The tiny flowers grow in small cream/yellow clusters at the tips of the branchlets. The fruits are quite small clusters of typical Melaleuca capsules containing fine seeds.

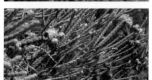

Paperbark Ti-tree occurs across central Cape York and is the dominant species in a limited area, already reduced to about 30% of its original size by human activity. It is one of the common trees of the Golden Shouldered Parrot's habitat.

48 Rusty Pittosporum

Pittosporum ferrugineum is one of six Pittosporums found in north Queensland, and it extends south to Wide Bay in SE Qld. It is also found north to India and east into the Pacific. It grows as a shrub or small tree, sometimes buttressed, and the underside of the leaves is clothed in pale rusty hairs. The flowers are white, cream or yellow and the yellow or orange fruit open to reveal about 15 orange or red sticky seeds (Above). In India Rusty Pittosporum has been used medicinally to control fevers, and it is also eaten, despite its toxic qualities. In Thailand it has been trialled successfully as a control for snail pests. Rusty Pittosporum occurs in swampy situations in Far North Queensland, as well as adjacent to mangroves and waterways, but can also be found on hilltops. Its seeds are eaten by Metallic Starlings.

Ht >20m   Lf 40-150mm   Fl any month 14-18mm   Fr Jun-Jan 10-18mm

49 Cottonwood

Hibiscus tiliaceus is a common tree near beaches, along coastal streams and in lowland swamps. Cottonwood has heart-shaped leaves with radiating veins, and large, bright yellow flowers with a deep red centre. Cottonwood belongs to the Hibiscus family, and occurs between Cape York and Port Macquarie, NSW, as well as in the NT. The fruits (Above) are rough and spiky. The tree is usually untidy in shape, tending to sprawl outwards, sending up new shoots through the tangled mass of branches. Aboriginal people used the straight suckering branches as light weight spear shafts, and the bark made a strong rope. In Tahiti three forms of the Cottonwood were known, and it was used in making tapa cloth, from the beaten bark, as well as a strong, woven cloth. Medicine made from the flowers was used to treat tonsilitis and also to heal abscesses. The name *'tiliaceus'* refers to the similarity of the leaves to those of Linden (*Tilia*) trees. In places where cottonwood trees overhang the water, fallen flowers can be seen floating delicately on the water below, a tropical icon.

Ht >12m   Lf 50-300mm   Fl Jul-Apr petals 40-80mm long   Fr Feb-Oct 15-28mm

50 Tulip Tree (Northern Cottonwood)

The Tulip Tree, *Thespesia populnea*, also known as the **Northern Cottonwood**, is very similar to the Cottonwood (above). While the flowers of both can darken with age, the Tulip Tree's flowers quickly become a dark red (Below). The seed pods are also much rounder and smoother than those of the Cottonwood, and even the dried fruits are still somewhat rounded (Right). The leaves are similar, but the Tulip Tree has shinier leaves than the Cottonwood, sparsely clothed with coppery scales, while the Cottonwood's leaves are hairy and pale on the under surface. Originating in India, the Tulip Tree is found across the Pacific to Hawaii, where the wood was valued for bowls. In Queensland it is found along the whole east coast. It is closely related to Cotton, with which it shares glands which produce the poison gossypol. The yellow juice from young fruit had many medicinal uses in India, and extracts from the flowers and fruits inhibit the growth of two bacteria, and may help lower high blood pressure.

Ht >10m   Lf 100-300mm   Fl Jan-Feb petals 50-65mm long   Fr Jul-Dec 20-35mm

51 Beach Sheoak

Casuarina equisetifolia is a common sight along beaches, where the branches, resembling Cassowary feathers, offer thin shade. Its needles are actually modified stems, with the leaves just tiny spurs. The fruit is a prickly cone, while male fruits are catkins shedding the wind dispersed pollen. The tree grows between Cape York and Mission Beach, and in SE Asia and the Pacific. As a pioneer species, it uses root nodules to fix nitrogen, and chemicals in the leaves suppress the growth of other plants. The dense wood is suitable for piles, fence posts and charcoal.

Ht >35m Lf needles5-13mm/node Fl Feb&Sep Fr Jun-Jan 10-24

52 Canthium

Cyclophyllum multiflorum (prev Canthium sp) is a shrub or small tree with layered branches, growing close to mangroves, but also found in rainforest to quite high altitudes. The leaves lie in pairs along square or flattened twigs, and show prominent looping veins. Masses of cream, yellow or orange flowers, at any time of year, are followed by attractive orange or red fruit. These resemble Coffee, which is a close relative. Canthium is found in a limited area from Cooktown to Paluma.

Ht >15m   Lf 45-130mm   Fl any month 9-14mm   Fr Aug-Mar 8-12mm

53 Indian Beech (Pongamia)

Millettia pinnata is an attractive tree of the beach rainforest, common at Cape Tribulation. It is deciduous, losing its leaves in October and rapidly growing new red leaves that can be quite spectacular. 3-7 thin leaflets make up a compound leaf. The pink or purple pea flowers are followed by brown pods containing 1 or 2 seeds. All parts of the plant are poisonous and cause nausea and vomiting if eaten. However the seeds contain 30-40% of an oil that was once used for cooking and lighting, and has great promise for biodiesel. Trials in India have shown huge potential for fuel production with existing technology (160kg pods/tree/year for >100years). A million tonnes of this oil are currently used for the production of soap and lubricants each year. As well there are numerous medicinal uses for compounds from Indian Beech, and the roots, as well as fixing nitrogen, are excellent for erosion control. An attractive street tree, planted in Cairns, it is found from Cape York to Paluma, near sea level, as well as through SE Asia to India and Pakistan. A close relative (no 438) is found on rivers in North Queensland.

Ht >20m   Lf 50-230mm (leaflet)   Fl Apr-Nov 10mm   Fr Sep-Apr 55-95mm

Shore & Swamp - Shrubs

54 Eastern Gondola Bush

Tabernaemontana orientalis is a shrub or small tree found close to the beach with distinctive gondola shaped fruits, often in pairs. The attractive white flowers are scented. The ripe fruits are orange, splitting to reveal fleshy red succulent arils, or seed coverings. Flowers and fruits are found throughout the year. The leaves are large with prominent veins, and are wider towards the apex. Eastern Gondola Bush is found in northern Qld, WA, and the NT. It is also found in PNG, Indonesia and Melanesia. It belongs to the same family as the well-known Frangipani. Aboriginal people used the white latex from broken stems to cure sores and ulcers, hence the other common name of **Iodine Bush** for this plant.

Ht >8m   Lf 50-200mm   Fl any month 14-35mm   Fr any month 17-30mm

55 Sea Lettuce Tree

Not a tree, not much like lettuce; but *Scaevola taccada* does grow by the sea. This bushy shrub with shiny whorls of leathery leaves grows right on the beach front. The small white flowers (Left) are attractively placed in the centre of the leaf clusters, and they are followed by whitish fruit (Right). The fruits are eaten by Cassowaries and Silver Eyes. The hand shaped flowers have given this genus its name, after the left handed Roman hero Caius Scaevola, who supposedly chose to burn off his right hand in a fire.

Ht >4m   Lf 45-220mm   Fl Aug-May Fr Jan-Oct 7-18mm

56 Beach Myrtella

Lithomyrtus obtusa is an attractive flowering shrub of the beach dunes, also found in rainforest and woodland near the coast. The bush grows small, velvety-hairy leaves that can turn reddish with recurved margins. The pink flowers are followed by reddish to blue-black berries. There are 11 species of Lithomyrtus, all found in Australia. Beach Myrtella occurs from Cape York to Bundaberg, and also in the NT and PNG.. This heath plant prefers exposed windy sites.

Ht >2.5m   Lf 15-45mm   Fl Jan-Sep 12-18mm Fr any month 5-10mm

57 Silver Bush

Sophora tomentosa is a world-wide inhabitant of tropical beaches, though the plant found in Australia may be a sub-species. The plant is densely clothed in fine hairs which give it a striking silver appearance. It is a shrub common on beaches and near mangroves, with compound leaves made up of from 9 to 19 rounded leaflets with very short stems. The yellow pea flowers are held on a spike. The unusual pods, like pearls on a string, have given the plant the name of 'Necklace Pod' in America. The buoyant seeds are carried by ocean currents for long distances. Silver Bush is found in Australia from Cape York to Port Macquarie in NSW, though it is listed as threatened in that state, a victim of invasive weeds and human destruction of its habitat. It contains the alkaloid Cytisine, discovered in 1818, which is an emetic and purgative toxin. The seeds are quite poisonous. The plant has been used as an ornamental in India and the USA, where it attracts birds and butterflies. The roots fix nitrogen, and the leaves make a good compost. It is salt and drought tolerant.

Ht >5m   Lf 22-60mm leaflets   Fl Dec-Jul 15mm   Fr May-Jan 60-200mm

58 Beach Berry Bush

Colubrina asiatica is a medium sized woody shrub with a sprawling habit, common on beaches. This shrub or scrambling vine can grow as much as 10m in a year, and has become a serious weed in some parts of the world such as the West Indies and Florida. It seeds heavily in as little as one year (with seeds remaining viable for several years), grows roots where stems touch the ground, and grows densely where stems are cut or damaged. In Australia it is a native, and is not considered a problem. The leaves alternate along the stems, and the small green flowers are followed by brown or grey fruit capsules that float on the sea. Each capsule contains three dark brown to black seeds. Beach Berry Bush is also known as 'Latherleaf' due to the ability of the leaves to substitute for soap. It has been used for medicine and as a fish poison in SE Asia, and the boiled leaves are eaten as a green in Thailand. Research in Taiwan has recently identified three new glycosides from this plant. It is found from Cape York to Bundaberg, as well as in the NT, and through SE Asia to Africa and also across the Pacific Islands.

Ht >10m+   Lf 30-100mm   Fl Apr-Jun 4-5mm   Fr any month 7-9mm

59 Tie Bush

Wikstroemia indica is a small twiggy shrub with slender branches, found on beaches as well as in open forest and rainforest from Cape York to the Illawarra district in NSW. Tie Bush also occurs through SE Asia to India, and in the Pacific Islands. New stems on this shrub are covered with fine hairs, and carry small shiny leaves on short leaf stalks. The flowers are green to yellowish green, without petals, and are followed by the bright orange or red fruits that are eaten by Mistletoebirds and Brown Cuckoo-doves. Tie Bush gets its name from the extemely strong fibres in the bark, which give a bush string. Another name is 'Bootlace Bush'. It is used to make high grade paper, suitable for bank notes, with $500,000 worth exported from the Philippines to China and Japan each year. It was a traditional medicine for treating wounds and cancers, and numerous medicinal compounds, including Wikstroemine, Daphnoretin, and two new biflavenoids that are active against drug resistant Malaria strains, have been identified. Japanese research has identified anti allergy properties, too.

Ht >4m   Lf 9-60mm   Fl Sep-Feb 8-18mm   Fr Dec-Jun 5-10mm

60 Coconut Palm

Tropical beaches bring to mind Coconut Palms (*Cocos nucifera*) overhanging the sand, and there are plenty near Cairns (Right). These are regularly stripped of their nuts, which if allowed to ripen and fall can be hazardous, even fatal. There has been much debate about whether coconuts are 'native' to Australia. In 1848 HMS Rattlesnake encountered fruiting coconuts on Frankland Island, (south of Cairns), and also on Barnard Island. Given that coconuts, especially those with thick husks, can survive a 3000 mile sea voyage and still germinate, it is possible that these were a natural introduction, though probably they were planted by Beche-de-mer fishermen. Fossil relatives 2 million years old are found in New Zealand and India, and it seems coconuts originated in the western Pacific. While the coconut provides an edible flesh, very digestible, and a pleasant drink, it became famous for its oil, which is a solid at room temperature. 'Nut lard', as it was known, became valuable when modern soap was patented in 1841, and after 1846 a by-product, glycerine, became even more valuable for the production of dynamite.

Ht >30m   Lf 700-1000mm 3-6m frond   Fl any month 12mm   Fr any month 200-300mm

61 Foxtail Palm

There is no doubt about the Australian origins of the Foxtail Palm, *Wodyetia bifurcata* (Left and Below), which originates from Cape Melville, north of Cooktown. Here the palms grow amongst huge granite boulders, within a National Park. The fronds are described as 'plumose', meaning fluffy, and the common name of 'foxtail' suits them perfectly. The trees are solitary and not clumping, and are easier to grow than the similar Black Palm (no 63). The fronds do not have the white or silver undersides seen in Black Palms. The fruits are orange to red when ripe, and are carried in large bunches (Left). Fruit are eaten by Giant White-tailed Rats and Feral Pigs.

As these very attractive palms became better known and sought after, their seeds became quite valuable. Not so many years ago there was a famous scandal when seed poachers with political connections were caught in the park, and those responsible for their apprehension seemed to suffer greater punishment for upholding the law than did the poachers for breaking it. Fortunately there is now plenty of seed produced outside the park, and the original trees should be safe once more.

The palms seen in Cairns and north to Cooktown are all planted as street and garden trees. These palms have become very fashionable overseas in places such as Florida where the climate suits them.

Ht >15m   Lf 90-107mm 2.6-3.2m fronds   Fl Jan-May 25-30mm   Fr Oct-Mar 47-65mm

62 Fan Palm

Licuala ramsayii is one of the world's most attractive palms, and it helps create the sense of magic of the Cape Tribulation rainforest. The large pleated leaves held on long stems are almost two metres across. It is common through lowland rainforest, often in swampy areas, but there are some occurrences at higher altitude. The palm on the right (Above) was part way up Mt Sorrow behind Cape Tribulation, and there are groves near Kuranda, 400 metres above sea level. Fan Palms occur between Cape York and the Paluma Range, north of Townsville. The Licuala palm provided Aboriginal people with an edible cabbage, and the leaves could be used for wrapping food or for thatch. Very young leaves were also used for cigarette papers.

Ht >20m   Lf 1.2-2m diameter   Fl Feb-Oct 2-3mm   Fr Nov-Feb 9-11mm

63 Black Palm (Duwar)

Normanbya normanbyi, named after an early Queensland Governor, is found in only a restricted area of North Queensland. It is a common palm in the Daintree area.

This is an elegant palm with a slim straight trunk and a small crown of compound leaves which are somewhat like the Foxtail Palm in that the leaflets surround the stalk. The stalks and the undersides of the leaves are whitish. Flowers are white or pink, and can be found under the palms along with the pink or red fallen fruits (Left). Male and female flowers never open together and pollination remains a mystery. The outside of the trunk is very hard and dense, and was traditionally used for spears and clap sticks, and in Papua New Guinea for flooring.

Ht >30m   Lf 300-600mm 2-4.3m fronds   Fl Apr-Nov 15-20mm   Fr Aug-Apr 30-50mm

Shore & Swamp - Vines

64 Matchbox Bean

Entada rheedii (3-4pair leaflets, >30mm wide) together with the very similar *Entada phaseoloides (1-2pair leaflets, 30mm+wide)* are reputed to be the largest vines growing in Australia. The large vine in the photo (Left) is on the path to the rocky headland at Trinity Beach. The seed pods are huge. The common name comes from the use made by early settlers of the flat brown seeds, which could be hollowed out to store the small wax matches of the time. In time small hinges and a catch were added, to make an impressive little container. This plant is found across tropical Africa, India, Asia and Australia, where it occurs on the lowlands north of Mackay. The seeds, known as "Sea Beans", wash up on beaches around the world. Tobacco made from these seeds was used in Africa to induce vivid dreams.

Lf 14-80mm   Fl Nov-Dec 5mm   Fr Jul-Nov >2m

65 Goats-foot Morning Glory

Ipomoea pes-caprae (Right), a vine, belongs to the same family as the familiar Morning Glory, as the flower and name would suggest. The 'goats-foot' refers to the unusual shape of the leaf, with its deeply notched end. The vine exudes white sap if broken, and bears a 4 valved, brown fruit capsule. It can root from the nodes. This is one of 18 species of Ipomoea found in the Wet Tropics. It is a hardy coloniser of beach front sand dunes, with seeds that float and are not affected by salt water. It is therefore found around all tropical oceans.

Lf 30-115mm   Fl any month 25-70mm
Fr Jul-Feb 10-20mm

66 Wild Grape

Ampellocissus acetosa is a vine or prostrate shrub, climbing by means of tendrils. It bears small maroon flowers (Sep-Dec) and black, grape-like fruit (Feb-May), though the name *acetosa*, meaning sour, should indicate that even if edible, the fruit may not be palatable. Do not sample local fruits that you do not know, as many are poisonous.

This vine (Right) was scrambling over rocks close to the sea, but it is also common in a variety of forest types close to sea level. The paired groups of three leaves with another leaf growing from the junction is characteristic. An inland species (*A. gardineri*) has similar leaves but with rusty hairs on the undersides.

Lf 30-130mm   Fl Sep-Dec 2-4mm   Fr Feb-May 6-13mm

67 Nicker Nut

Caesalpinia bonduc is an extremely thorny vine or scrambling shrub found on beaches. It grows large (>500mm) bipinnate leaves of 3-11 pairs of pinnae, each with 6-11 pairs of rounded leaflets with hooked thorns along the leaf stems. The main branches are also covered in prickles. The flowers are yellow or cream and produce green to brown spiny pods containing 1 or 2 shiny grey or bluish seeds. These can be used as beads or marbles, and the name 'Nicker' comes from an old English term for a marble. Nicker Nuts are found from Cape York to SE Qld, and on Lord Howe Island off NSW where it is now threatened. It also occurs in the NT and WA and around the tropical world, as the seeds float and are spread by ocean currents. The seeds were roasted, ground and boiled to produce a medicine that treated Malaria, and was effective as a diuretic, for diabetes, and for hypertension.

Ht >5m long   Lf 10-75mm   Fl Apr-Jul 12-24mm
Fr Apr-Nov 30-90mm

68 Opilia

Opilia amentacea is a vine which carries numerous cream or yellow fruits between Oct and Jan. It is a scrambler or twiner and is a root parasite, attaching to the roots of another plant. The shiny leaves are simple with several pairs of conspicuous lateral veins, and a mid rib that is raised on the underside. It grows tiny cream or yellow-green fragrant flowers while the fruits are largely composed of a large seed. The fruits were reportedly eaten by Aboriginal people and by the natives of Sudan, where it also occurs. (Do not risk eating native fruits you are not completely sure of, as many are very poisonous.) In Australia this vine occurs between Cape York and just north of Cairns. It is also found in the Northern Territory where it is the host of a fruit fly that was confused with the pest, the Oriental Fruit Fly. It has various medicinal uses in the Ivory Coast, and is used as an enema in Nigeria. Aboriginal people in the NT produced a yellow to orange dye from this vine, and in India it was used to treat dandruff. It is found through Asia to Africa, and grows in mountain thickets in China.

Ht >30m long   Lf 50-160mm   Fl Aug-Jan   Fr Oct-Jan 12-30mm

69 Thick-leaved Rhaphidophora

Rhaphidophora hayi is a climber adhering to trees in the swamp at Dubuji boardwalk near Cape Tribulation. The glossy alternating leaves are striking and attractive, but it appears that this vine has been little used as a garden plant. The Thick-leaved Rhaphidophora is found near sea level from the Bloomfield River to Innisfail. It bears minute yellow flowers clustered on a spike, but the fruit is not known here, though probably resembling a small Monsteria, to which it is related.

Lf 70-200mm   Fl Oct on spike 55-80mm
Fr unknown

70 Native Cardamon

Hornstedtia scottiana is a ginger-lke herb growing to 4 metres, with vivid pink or red fruits. These can appear to glow in the low light swampy situations which these plants favour, such as the Marrdja boardwalk near Cape Tribulation. The flowers have three petals, and the fruit capsules produce numerous small black or brown seeds, with a flavour resembling the spice Cardamon. Native Cardamon grows between Iron Range and Ingham, and also occurs in PNG, Vanuatu and the Solomon Islands. The fruits are eaten by Scrub Turkeys and Cassowaries, and Aboriginal people reportedly ate the seeds and pulp, and used the leaves for wrapping food. This is also a host plant for the small Banded Demon butterfly.

Ht >4m   Lf 300-700mm   Fl Jul-Jan 15-20mm   Fr Jan-Mar 10-25mm

71 Mother-in-Law's Tongue (Weed)

Sansevieria trifasciata (Left) is a familiar houseplant that has adapted to life on the beach. A poisonous member of the lily family from Africa, it grows sword like mottled leaves (>1m) and rare white flowers.

72 Mother of Millions (Air Plant) (Weed)

Bryophyllum pinnatum (Right) is a garden plant from Madagascar that has naturalised near beaches. Broken leaves can grow small plantlets on their margins. The maroon flowers are bell like. Plants (>1m) produce analgesic and anti-ulcer compounds.

73 Caustic Bush

Sarcostemma viminale (Left) is a succulent without visible leaves, with smooth stems and white to yellow flowers (Jan-Nov). It is a desert plant that grows on rocks and trees near the coast. It contains many chemicals, including glycosides, in a milky sap.

74 Pig Weed

Portulaca oleracea (Right) is a low spreading succulent, with fleshy leaves and stems. It grows in pockets of soil on rock, close to the sea. It is an Australian native (not Tas) but is grown and eaten around the world. It contains oxalic acid (which can be toxic) and omega 3 fatty acids, and has been used to treat internal parasites.

75 Bulrush

There are two species of *Typha* growing in North Queensland, *Typha domingensis* and *Typha orientalis*, difficult to tell apart. They are perennial plants, growing in water with their roots in the mud, and the leaves separating below water level and standing up to 3 metres tall. The narrow leaves contain air-filled spaces which makes them strong, light and buoyant. The flowers are carried on spikes that emerge from the middle of the leaf clusters, the male flowers above the female. They develop into a brown cylindrical mass of seeds, dispersed by wind, each seed developing a parachute of fine hairs. Bulrushes are found in all Australian states and around the world in warm temperate and tropical areas. They can become a problem in drains and irrigation channels, where they block the flow of water. Aboriginal people ate most parts of the plant, and the leaves and roots are diuretic. 'Cumbungi' is an alternative widely used name for Bulrush, and probably comes from the Wiradjuri language. The species shown here is probably *T. domingensis*, which has narrower leaves, tolerates saline water, and occurs worldwide.

Ht >3m   Lf .6-3m   Fl Sep-May   Spike 5-20mm wide   Fr dates not known

76 Sedges

Sedges are grass-like herbs, annual or perennial, often forming small tufts or clumps. Belonging to the family Cyperaceae, many come from the genus *Cyperus*, though it can be difficult to discriminate between the many different genera without a microscope. The sedges shown were growing close to mangroves on the Northern Beaches near Cairns. (Left - *Fimbristylis ferruginea*;   Right - *Cyperus javanicus*) Sedges have little economic importance, though some grow starchy edible tubers, and the earliest paper was made from a sedge - *Cyperus papyrus*. They help stabilise marshy areas and filter water.

77 Sand Couch (Salt-water Couch)

Sporobolus virginicus is a couch like grass that grows on sand adjacent to beaches or on the highly saline marsh soils adjacent to mangroves. In NSW the name "Sand Couch' is used for varieties with leaves wider than 1mm, and **Marine Couch** for varieties with leaves less than 1mm wide. Sand couch can grow to 500mm in height, but is commonly less than this, and the plants photographed were only about 300mm high (at Holloway's Beach).

Sand Couch occurs in all mainland Australian states, mainly on beaches, but also inland, in shallow depressions or seasonal lakes. It is also found in Africa, India, Sri Lanka and the USA. It is a good grazing grass for cattle, if well managed, and can tolerate limited flooding. It has glands which excrete salt, hence its high salt tolerance, which is making it increasingly attractive as a turf grass for sports fields in saline areas. It has long been used to protect sand dunes, but will also grow on clay soils. Traditional medicinal uses include its use as a gargle, and for relief of urinary irritations.

78 Scrub Breadfruit

Pandanus monticola is a common plant in Rainforest near the beach. Like most Pandanus species, the leaves are very long and spiny. As the spines are pointing forwards along the leaf, they are not so inclined to catch at you as they would be if they curved back. The edges of the leaf near the base are spineless, but there are rows of spines on the midrib under the leaf, as well as two rows on top near the apex. The trunk is quite thin (Left), about 50mm in diameter, and without prop roots. The fruit, from Mar to Sep, is red when ripe, with hundreds of spiky segments making up a grapefruit sized ball. Near Cape Tribulation this Pandanus is the host of the Peppermint Stick Insect (Above) which lies in the centre groove of a leaf with its legs extended fore and aft - the iconic insect of the Daintree area.

Ht >10m   Lf .8-2.3m   Fl Nov-Dec?   Fr Mar-Sep 60-120mm

79 Sedge

Scirpodendron ghaeri is not closely related to the Scrub Breadfruit (Above) yet at first glance it is almost indistinguishable from it. Growing in swamps close to the beach, it is a common plant at the Dubuji Boardwalk near Cape Tribulation.

Like the Scrub Breadfruit, the leaves are very long and lined with fine spikes. However, those on the sedge are finer and less thorny than on the Pandanus. Where the Pandanus grows a whitish stem or trunk that can be quite tall, the sedge does not form a trunk, and the leaves radiate from the butt.

This sedge appears to grow only in very wet areas, often in stagnant water, as in the photograph (Right). While the Scrub Breadfruit may be growing only a few metres away, it is usually on dry ground, and in fact thrives quite a distance up the nearby mountains.

There appears to be little information readily available about this sedge, though it is widespread in the Pacific and South East Asian area, with occurrances in the Caroline Islands, Hawaii, Thailand and Sri Lanka.

80 Beach Pandan

Pandanus tectorius is one of 14 species of Pandanus found in or adjacent to the rainforest of Far North Queensland. This is a common Pandanus on or near beaches, the one shown (Right) is at the Thala Beach Lodge near Port Douglas.

The tree grows with tight whorls of large strap like leaves, thorny along the edges and mid rib, especially towards the apex. Sharp conical nodules dot the trunk, and there can be prop roots up to 2 metres long with a few spines. The fruits are large and composed of many 5 to 7 cornered segments (Below), each containing some 5 to 20 seeds. They may hang on the tree up to a year, are yellow or orange when ripe, and are eaten by Palm Cockatoos. They were also eaten by Aboriginal people. In Micronesia the tips of the prop roots were also eaten, and the leaves woven, and used for thatch and sails.

Ht >12m   Lf 800-1700mm   Fr May-Dec 120-180mm

Steve Hurst @ USDA-NRCS Plants Database

81 Swamp Pandan

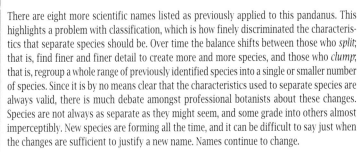

Pandanus solmslaubachii is a large tree with spiny conical nodules on the trunk. Like the Beach Pandan (Above) it can have prop roots, though this is not always the case. The leaves can be very long and are spiny along the edges and mid rib from about the middle to the apex. These plants were first collected along the Endeavour River. The fruits are very large and composed of many 4 to 7 cornered segments. The outside of each segment is hard and dry, orange when ripe. The inside is a waxy yellow and smells of banana mixed with acetate. These fruits are eaten by the Giant White-tailed Rat, whose teeth can cut through almost anything of interest, including power cables and tin cans.

There are eight more scientific names listed as previously applied to this pandanus. This highlights a problem with classification, which is how finely discriminated the characteristics that separate species should be. Over time the balance shifts between those who *split*, that is, find finer and finer detail to create more and more species, and those who *clump*, that is, regroup a whole range of previously identified species into a single or smaller number of species. Since it is by no means clear that the characteristics used to separate species are always valid, there is much debate amongst professional botanists about these changes. Species are not always as separate as they might seem, and some grade into others almost imperceptibly. New species are forming all the time, and it can be difficult to say just when the changes are sufficient to justify a new name. Names continue to change.

Ht >20m   Lf 1-4m   Fr Jul-Nov 120-300mm

41

82 Sword Fern

Nephrolepis acutifolia is a striking epiphytic fern at Marrdja Boardwalk near Cape Tribulation, where these magnificent specimens (Right) were growing above a swamp. The pinnae, or leaflets, are closely spaced along the mid rib, on fronds which may be up to several metres long. They have rounded scalloped teeth, and the sori bearing the spores are in a narrow band along the edges of the leaflets. Normally this fern grows in exposed rocky situations, with upright fronds to just 700mm long.

Sword Fern occurs in North-eastern Queensland and throughout SE Asia and the Pacific, and even in tropical Africa. It is an excellent pot or basket fern, but will not tolerate frost. It has been grown overseas as an understory crop for its ornamental fronds.

83 Drynaria Fern (Oak Leaf Fern)

Drynaria sparsisora is a fern that grows in large masses (Below) close to mangroves and beach, yet is sometimes found in rainforest (Left). It is a large handsome fern, with two distinct types of leaf. The short and wide nest leaves may be lobed (like oak leaves), and are held erect at the base of the plant. They collect debris to form humus, as well as protecting the rhizomes (or stems) from the sun. They persist on the plant, even when dried and papery. The large (>700mm) pinnate (or branching) fronds carry the spores, scattered on the under-surface of the leaflets. Drynaria Fern is found in NE Qld north of Bundaberg, growing on rocks, trees and on the ground. It also grows in SE Asia and was used to treat asthma in Sabah. (see also no 183 - Oak Leaf Fern)

84 Ribbon Fern

Ophioglossum pendulum is a simple but attractive fern which usually grows from the peat accumulated by a Platycerium fern (See no 288). Ribbon Fern has a fleshy, white, creeping rhizome, from which hang the bright green, straplike fronds (>900mm). These fronds are fleshy but brittle, and usually twisted or kinked. Fertile fronds are shorter, sausage like and ribbed. Ribbon Fern occurs from north Qld to the Hunter River in northern NSW. It also occurs through Indonesia and SE Asia to Madagascar, and has become naturalised in Florida and Hawaii. Germinating spores have a symbiotic relationship with a fungus. The scientific name means 'Adder's Tongue', and the fern is sometimes called 'Old World Adder's Tongue'. It had medicinal uses in India.

85 Mistletoe (Butterfly Plant)

Dendrophthoe curvata is one of several types of mistletoe that are easily viewed on the generally stunted beachfront trees. The plant can be pendulous, or spreading; the elongated leaves showing a clear mid-rib and faint side veins. The flowers can be orange, red or pink with yellow tips, and the fruits are red to yellow berries. This mistletoe has many hosts, including the paperbark (Left). It occurs from the Jardine River at Cape York to Eungella, near Mackay, and also across SE Asia and India to Africa. While mistletoes are parasitic on their hosts, this species is the host for two butterflies, the 'Union Jack' and 'Margarita's Blue'.

Lf 60-130mm Fl any month 28-60mm Fr Jul-Dec 10-14mm

86 Miquel's Mistletoe (Butterfly Plant)

Amyema miquelii is a straggly mistletoe that favours Eucalypts. It is quite spindly, with elongated pale leaves having a few poorly defined veins running lengthwise. Flowers can be red or orange. This is a common Australian mistletoe, with the greatest number of recorded host species. It has been increasing in Eucalypts in Southern Australia, and is sometimes blamed for their deaths, though it is not in the interests of mistletoes to kill their hosts. Indeed, it is thought they can co-exist for some hundreds of years. It is the host to several of the 'Blue' butterflies, including some rare species, that also involve harmless 'Sugarants' in their life cycle. Pollination is by birds, and there are mistletoes that grow on this mistletoe, and compete for the birds' attention.

Other plants found on the beaches or in the swamps.

This is a partial list of plants included in other sections in this book that may occur on the coast or in swamps. Mangroves have not been listed again. The numbers refer to the plant listing number in the book, then to pages. Many plants grow across the boundaries we label as habitats. Plants seemingly just don't read the books that say where they should be found.

TREES: Moreton Bay Ash *(Corymbia tessellaris)* #91 p46   Swamp Mahogany *(Lophostemon suaveolans)* #120 p57   Glossy Tamarind *(Guoia acutifolia)* #129 p60   Bushman's Clothes Pegs *(Grevillea glauca)* #379 p149   Geebung *(Persoonia falcata)* #391 p153   White Apple *(Syzygium forte)* #440 p170

PALMS: Nypa Palm *(Nypa fruticans)* #18 p17   Kennedy Palm *(Corypha utan)* #138 p63

VINES: Native Jasmine *(Jasminum elongatum)* #153 p68   Common Hoya *(Hoya australis)* #316 p126   Derris *(Derris sp* (Daintree)*)* #414 p161

ORCHIDS: Golden Orchid *Durabaculum undulatum (Prev. Dendrobium discolor)* #28 p21   Pencil Orchid *(Dockrillia teretifolia)* #163 p72

Coastal Open Forest

COASTAL OPEN FOREST

Visitors to North Queensland come expecting to see the reef and rainforest, each inscribed on the World Heritage register as very special places. Yet between Cairns and Kuranda the rainforest belt is barely 10 kilometers wide, and there are vast expanses of open forest on the drier, inland side of this narrow corridor. Even on the coast, where rainfall is generally high, there are large areas of open forest. This is composed of an upper storey of larger trees, somewhat scattered, so that plenty of light penetrates, and a lower storey of small trees and shrubs below which is a mix of grasses, vines and other low growing plants. Looking at the wooded hillsides around Cairns, it is easy to see the division between these open forests and the rainforest. The open forests are a dull grey green, often extending up the ridges almost to the top of the range, while the denser green of the rainforests is dominant on the higher mountains and in gullies and along streams where there is more protection. What really divides the two, though, is fire. Open forests burn, while on the whole rainforest does not. The quite sharp division commonly seen between the two is actually a line defined by fire. This margin moves back and forth over the years, advancing into the rainforest where fires are regular, and moving the other way when burning is limited.

It is now thought that Aboriginal burning has had a profound effect on the vegetation of most of Australia. Eucalypts, paperbarks and wattles are families that have benefited from burning, and are now dominant across much of the country. An area of open forest usually consists of just a few species from these families, much as woods in England are composed generally of a few dominant species, with a few less common trees scattered through them. The rainforests are incredibly more diverse, and it is rare to find stands of one species within them. Given control of fire, it is likely that a considerable amount of the open forest around Cairns would quite quickly revert to rainforest. An interesting example of this shifting boundary is visible above the Cairns-Kuranda railway line. Here fires sparked by steam engines in years past have burnt uphill from the line, as fire burns more strongly uphill. With the replacement of steam engines by diesel locomotives, fire is now much less common here, and rainforest is beginning to reclaim these areas.

There has been intense debate about how best to manage fire within national parks. If burning is not carried out, there will be a change in the vegetation, and therefore the wildlife, from what was present when the park was declared. Not burning also raises the potential for very hot fires which consume the increased fuel built up over the years without fire. Such fires do more damage than regular controlled burns. However controlled burns, especially if they are late in the season and cover large areas, do considerable damage. Freshly burnt areas are at least temporarily quite unattractive, and fires also kill some wildlife. Open forest has until now proven more vulnerable to weed infestation than rainforest. Many of the plant species found in open forest are weeds, such as Lantana, which find the more open conditions to their liking.

While it is convenient to group plants under this 'Coastal Open Forest' heading, remember there is much overlap between coastal and inland open forest, and that near Cooktown the distinction becomes almost meaningless. Many rainforest plants grow in open forest until a fire kills them, but as they stand out more in open forest they have been included here.

Coastal Open Forest - Eucalypts

87 White Gum

Eucalyptus platyphylla has a smooth, white to silvery white trunk after the bark is shed late in the year. Old bark becomes pink or reddish. The leaves are broad, almost fan shaped, and are often dropped during the dry season (wintering). The tree grows to a medium size. Trees on the coast (Right) can have quite pendulous to weeping branches. (See p 145 for an inland tree.) White Gum is found from Rockhampton to Cape York,

along the east coast and hinterland. It dominates areas of poorly aerated, infertile soils between Cooktown and Lakeland Downs, which are flooded during the Wet season.

Ht >20m+   Lf C60x50mm   Fl Aug-Nov   Fr 7-8mm

88 Molloy Red Box

Eucalyptus leptophleba (Right) is the dominant tree on Hartley's Creek where it flows through open forest near the Cook Highway. It also dominates some areas between Cooktown and Lakeland Downs. It has a softish, slightly tessellated bark, extending to the branches. The trunks are grey with a slight red or pinkish hue evident at times; a typical 'Box' bark, rather featureless compared to many of the other Eucalypts. The leaves are narrow and the flowers are a dense cream to white mass of stamens, followed by small gum nuts (Above). This tree is found throughout most of Cape York Peninsula, and also occurs in New Guinea. It has been planted in Zimbabwe where it has grown well. In Australia, it has been used to produce apricot, light brown and dark grey dyes.

Ht >25m   Lf >240x30mm   Fl Mar-Aug   Fr >11mm

89 Clarkson's Bloodwood

Corymbia clarksoniana (prev. *Eucalyptus clarksoniana*) is a widely distributed tree throughout eastern Queensland, which extends into northern NSW and also PNG. The white flowers (Mar-Jul) are followed by urn shaped gum nuts (Above). It can dominate wet to very wet lowland alluvial soils, which are well drained. South of Cairns, it provides Mahogany Glider habitat, and is also common near Cooktown.

Ht >20m   Lf >180x25mm   Fl Mar-Jul   Fr >20x15mm

90 Pink Bloodwood

Corymbia intermedia resembles Clarkson's Bloodwood (no 89) but is confined mostly to the coast and nearby ranges from Newcastle (NSW) to Cape York. The leaves are wider and the bark is rough, with the leaves darker on one side. Flowers are white to cream, and the gum nuts (Right) are often speckled, and generally wider towards the base. The timber is not generally milled, but is used for fence posts.

Ht 20-30m   Lf 90-160x15-30mm   Fl Nov-Jan Fr 10-20x10-15mm

91 Moreton Bay Ash

Corymbia tessellaris almost always shows an abrupt division between the tessellated (breaking into squarish sections) bark on the lower one to four metres of trunk, and the smooth grey or white bark on the upper trunk (Right). The trees grow quickly to more than 20m, and this is one of the trees likely to take advantage of increased carbon dioxide in the atmosphere. It is native to most of eastern Queensland.

The leaves are narrow and tend to hang downwards (Left) sometimes with a drooping appearance. They are dull green with veins at about 45 degrees to the mid vein. The flowers are white or cream, small, and grow in clusters. They attract Rainbow Lorikeets and bees. Buds are pear shaped and the gum nuts are thin walled and cylindrical or urn shaped. Moreton Bay Ash is widespread in the area, usually in small numbers. Another common name is **Carbeen**.

Ht 12-35m   Lf 10-200x7-20mm   Fl Nov-Feb   Fr 5-12x5-9mm

92 Cape York Red Gum

Eucalyptus brassiana is a common Eucalypt around Cooktown, found in the botanic gardens and at the foot of Mt.Cook. It grows as far south as Helenvale. The lower bark is dark and quite rough and ridged, while the upper trunk and limbs are smooth white or yellowish, with the bark peeling in strips. The tree (Left) usually has a pronounced lean to one side. It is found across Cape York and in New Guinea. The adult leaves are long and lance shaped, a slightly glossy green, densely veined, with a yellow or red mid vein. The buds have a long pointed cap, and the flowers are white. The gum nuts are hemispherical, with four sharp protruding points. Cape York Red Gum is most likely to be found on poor soils, either on flats that flood during the wet season, or on rocky slopes. The wood is used in ply, for posts, and in general construction. The trees provide good shade and pollen for bees.

Ht >30m   Lf 180x25mm   Fl Jan   Fr 14x12mm

Coastal Open Forest - Eucalypts

93 Blue Gum

Also known as **Forest Red Gum**, *Eucalyptus tereticornis* is a tall tree with a white, blue grey or silver trunk (Right). The base of the tree shown is still losing its old bark and, though stained, does not retain a distinct skirt of rough bark. Sometimes the trunk and limbs turn silver (Left), and can look glorious in the moonlight. This medium to tall tree is found from Northern NSW to Cooktown, along the east coast and hinterland. The buds are covered with a horn shaped operculum, or cap, and the flowers are white, rarely pink. The fruits are small, rounded gum nuts with four outward pointed teeth (Below, Right). It provides a hard, red, durable timber. On the Walsh River intermediate forms of the Blue Gum and the related River Red Gum (*E. camaldulensis*) can be found. Blue Gum has been hugely successful as a plantation timber in many overseas countries. It can grow to 50m in 7 years in Brazil, and in Argentina up to 30 cubic metres of timber per hectare per year is produced on a 10 year cycle. It is also used for the production of charcoal, firewood, pulp, pilings and construction timber. However it is now a weed in California and the pollen dominates the pollen count of parts of India; bad news for asthmatics. In Australia it provides nectar for bees and food for koalas.

Ht 20-50m   Lf 100-200x 10-27mm   Fl Apr-Oct   Fr 6-8mm

Forest &
Kym Starr
USGS

94 Cadaghi

Corymbia torelliana (prev. *Eucalyptus torelliana*) is one of the few Eucalypts which lives in rainforest, where it is easily distinguished due to the smooth greenish bark of the upper trunk and limbs. Although originally found in only a small area between Cooktown and Ingham, this species has proven very adaptable as an ornamental street tree in inland New South Wales, for example, where it is now considered an invasive weed. The seedlings (Below, Centre) are soft and covered with reddish hairs. Although mature leaves are longer and narrower than the juvenile leaves (Left), it is common for even large trees to retain their rounded juvenile leaves. The timber is hard and very heavy, and contains gum veins. Masses of white flowers precede rounded 'gum nut' fruit. The smooth bark is shed late in the year. The trees shown still have a few flakes of the old bark attached. The Cadaghi has a unique seed dispersal mechanism, called 'mellitochory', in which the seeds are spread by small and stingless native bees. The tree also poisons the soil around it so that only the seeds that fall at a distance from the trunk will germinate.

Ht 20-30m   Lf 90-160mm(Int) 100-140mm(adult-rare)   Fl Sep-Oct   Fr 9-14mm

47

Coastal Open Forest - Eucalypts

95 Red Stringybark

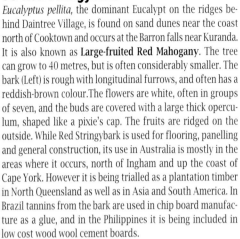

Eucalyptus pellita, the dominant Eucalypt on the ridges behind Daintree Village, is found on sand dunes near the coast north of Cooktown and occurs at the Barron falls near Kuranda. It is also known as **Large-fruited Red Mahogany**. The tree can grow to 40 metres, but is often considerably smaller. The bark (Left) is rough with longitudinal furrows, and often has a reddish-brown colour.The flowers are white, often in groups of seven, and the buds are covered with a large thick operculum, shaped like a pixie's cap. The fruits are ridged on the outside. While Red Stringybark is used for flooring, panelling and general construction, its use in Australia is mostly in the areas where it occurs, north of Ingham and up the coast of Cape York. However it is being trialled as a plantation timber in North Queensland as well as in Asia and South America. In Brazil tannins from the bark are used in chip board manufacture as a glue, and in the Philippines it is being included in low cost wood wool cement boards.

Ht >40m   Lf 100-160mm   Fl Dec-Feb   Fr 14-17mm

96 Scarlet Gum

Eucalyptus phoenicia is a most attractive flowering Eucalypt found in a small area north of Cooktown growing on sandstone. It has also been reported south of the Bloomfield River. It mainly occurs in the Northern Territory and extends into Western Australia. The tree is often small and can have multiple stems, with rough, flaky and fibrous bark, except on the small branches which are smooth. The leaf stalks are flattened. Up to 20 flowers can occur on a branch, forming a spherical mass. The bunches of buds are on long tapering stalks (Below, Left). The fruits are urn shaped, with a distinct neck (Right). Scarlet Gum has potential for the cut flower market, as the flowers are long lasting. It can be grown easily from seed. The tree is rich in euglobals. Around Katherine in the Northern Territory, it is the preferred source of timber for making didgeridus, and there is concern about the number of trees being used for this purpose. Scarlet Gum can be found in Cooktown in Boundary Street (Right), adjacent to a Caravan Park near the river end. Flowering is from Apr-Aug, with a few later blooms.

Ht 6-12m   Lf 80-120mm   Fl Apr-Aug
Fr 19-30mm

97 Yellow Wattle (Butterfly Plant)

Acacia flavescens is a common wattle in coastal areas, easily identified by its large leaves (actually phyllodes or flattened stems) which have 1-5 small teeth on the longer edge, close to where prominent veins end. The ball flowers are a pale yellow and the fruit is a flat pod, brown when ripe (Aug-Nov). The trees grow rapidly in cultivation. The seeds of Yellow Wattle are eaten by Crimson Rosellas. Three butterflies use this tree as a host plant.

Ht >20m Lf 90-300mm Fl Jan-Jun Fr 60-160mm

98 Spike Wattle

Acacia polystachya is a common wattle in open forests near Port Douglas, being a dominant species on Hartley's Creek. Young stems are three cornered and often red in colour (Right), though they can also be green. The leaves are long and shiny, and the swollen leaf stalk has a gland near the base. The tree prefers alluvial soil near watercourses or beaches. The flowers are white to yellow spikes. The fruits (Sep-Dec) are long pods which are twisted and often crimped between the seeds. Spike Wattle occurs betwen Cape York and Cairns.

Ht >25m Lf 75-250mm Fl Apr-Nov Fr 30-130mm

99 Broadleaf Salwood

Acacia mangium "is the most commercially important and widely planted tropical acacia", used to reclaim degraded Blady Grass infested land in SE Asia. The tree grows very rapidly and flowers and fruits profusely. The leaves have three or four prominent veins. The white to cream rod like flowers are followed by long twisted pods (Sep-Nov) containing shiny black seeds. The timber is hard, olive to gray brown, and works well. It is used for furniture and firewood, and makes excellent particle board. Also known as **Mangium** and **Black Wattle**, it grows near sea level from Ingham to Cape York, and in PNG and Indonesia.

Ht >30m Lf110-270mm Fl May-Jun Fr 120mm

Coastal Open Forest - Wattles

100 Silky Wattle

Acacia holosericea is one of about 950 wattle species found in Australia. The leaves are actually flattened stems, known as phyllodes, rather broad and covered with white silky hairs, giving them a somewhat silvery appearance. Usually three or four veins in the leaf are prominent, and the stems are 3-ribbed. The foliage can be rather dense, providing good shade, and the pods are long but tangled in a reddish mass, making it one of the easier wattles to identify. Silky wattle has fluffy, yellow flower spikes and occurs between Coen and Rockhampton as well as in the NT and WA. It is much used in Africa for fuel, windbreaks, and even as food (the roasted seeds are very nutritious). Aborigines used it as a fish poison.

Ht >8m   Lf 65-250mm   Fl Apr-Oct   Fr Aug-Oct 30-120mm

101 Daintree Wattle

Acacia cincinnata is an easy to identify wattle growing into a quite large tree. The leaves have three dominant veins which follow the shorter margin before separating. Leaves are smooth or covered in gold or silver hairs, and have a gland at the base. The tightly coiled pods are distinctive, and follow rod like cream to yellow flowers. Daintree Wattle is found between Rossville near Cooktown and SE Qld, though mainly on the edge of rainforest on or near the Atherton Tableland and nearby coast. It can be seen at the Barron Falls lookout near Kuranda. It has been trialled for fuel production in SE Asia and Africa, and has some potential in hybrid breeding programs for tropical acacia species.

Ht >30m   Lf 110-160mm   Fl Apr-Jun   Fr Jul-Feb 15-40mm

102 Red Bead Tree

Adenanthera pavonina is notable for its bright red seeds which grow in long dark pods with yellow interiors. The pods twist and split open in an untidy tangle, revealing the seeds. This is a rainforest tree found in nearby open forest, usually as a small tree, though it can grow tall. The leaves are compound, the smooth oval leaflets carried on each side of a mid rib. The leaves can have a slightly blueish colouration. The tree is deciduous, losing its leaves in Jul and Aug. This species normally occurs fairly close to sea level (up to 200m altitude) in North Queensland between Cape York and Cardwell. The seeds of this tree, also known as **Coral Bean Tree,** are remarkably uniform in weight (4 to a gram). The seeds have been used as an intoxicant, though poisonous, and in India it is used as a medicine. In Java the seeds are eaten after roasting, and the red marks placed on the foreheads of Brahmins are derived from this plant. It occurs across SE Asia extending to China and Australia. It has become a weed in some Pacific nations, and is banned in Florida.

Ht >30m   Lf 32-180 (leaflets)   Fl Jan 4mm   Fr May-Dec 200-250mm

Coastal Open Forest - Figs

103 Small-fruited Fig

Ficus microcarpa has simple shiny leaves. It can grow as a strangler or banyan and reach heights of 20 metres. The fruit is quite small, without a stalk, about 10mm across, spherical and shiny. It ripens to cream, yellow, orange, red, black or purple (Below, Right). Ripe fruit can be found most of the year. Small-fruited Fig is a native of Australia, but also occurs naturally in China, India, Sri Lanka, and New Caledonia. It has been spread around the Pacific, where it is becoming a weed on some islands. In Hawaii it is widely established, and due to its dense shade it tends to smother other vegetation. In Florida it is now considered an invasive weed.

The Small-fruited Fig is also known as the **Chinese Banyan Tree**, and often begins life as an epiphyte, the seed having been deposited on a branch of an existing tree. The thin roots that form grow down to the ground, gradually forming a network of interconnected roots that appear to strangle the host tree. The branches also can produce pillar like roots, so that the tree eventually grows very large. Pollination requires a specific wasp. This tree can be found along Spring Creek, a tributary of the Mowbray River. Numerous birds eat the fruits.

Ht >20m   Lf 30-120mm   Fr Nov-Aug 8-10mm

104 Small-leaved Fig

Ficus obliqua varies from a low canopy over rocks on coastal cliffs near the Rex Lookout on the way to Port Douglas to a huge strangler fig in rainforest, growing to 50 metres. It grows small glossy leaves on longish stalks, and produces small yellow, orange or red fruits on short stems. The fruits are eaten by many birds. Like other figs, the fruits are pollinated by a species of wasp, this wasp only attracted to this fig. Most seedlings start as an epiphyte, growing in a pocket of humus in another tree. About 5% of trees in an area are likely to host a fig, with deciduous trees more likely to be selected.

The Small-leaved Fig is found along the coast of Queensland and into South East Asia and the Pacific Islands.

Ht >50m   Lf 17-130mm   Fr any month 4-12mm

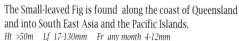

105 Sandpaper Fig

The leaves of *Ficus opposita* do indeed feel like sandpaper, being either hairy or sandpapery on both sides. The somewhat rounded leaves vary in length, and the tree may be lush (Right) or merely a few bare stems with a few scattered fruit attached, depending on the location and climate. Juvenile leaves can be narrow and lobed. The fruits are hairy on stems 4-10mm long, and turn pink, purple, red or black (Below) as they ripen. This sandpaper fig grows from southern Queensland across northern Australia and in PNG and SE Asia. The leaves were used by

Aboriginal people as sandpaper, the sap was used as a cure for ringworm, and the inner bark was used as a string. The fruits were eaten, and fire sticks were made from suitable stems. Many species of birds also eat the fruits.

Ht >10m   Lf 45-160mm   Fr Oct-Jun 10-20mm

106 Brown Macaranga (Butterfly Plant)

Macaranga mallotoides is an open shrub or small tree with large heart shaped leaves on thin spreading branches. There are three main veins in the leaf, with both sides hairy, especially underneath, and 2 or 4 smooth brown glands on the top of the leaf near where the stem is attached. Sometimes the stem is attached towards the centre of the leaf, and not on the edge. Several species of Macaranga occur in rainforest in North Queensland. They, along with many other rainforest species, are often found as under-story plants in the open forest, though rarely as large trees, suggesting that they succumb to burning.

Brown Macaranga occurs from Cape York to near Rockhampton, and in the NT. It was first collected near the Endeavour River by Banks and Solander in 1770, while "HMS Endeavour" was being repaired. The timber is soft and light, and the tree is the host of the Blue Moonbeam butterfly, whose caterpillars hide close to a vein under the leaf.

Ht >15m   Lf 32-220x22-235mm   Fl any month   Fr Nov-Feb 4-20mm

107 Blush Macaranga (Butterfly Plant)

Macaranga tanarius has peltate leaves, meaning the stem is attached towards the centre of the leaf. Leaves vary greatly in size, and cluster at the ends of the thin spreading branches. While the top of the leaves is shiny, underneath a mass of tiny whitish hairs causes the surface to look white. The leaf stalks can be quite short, or long as illustrated. It can be found in open forest as a tall shrub but grows to a tree in rainforest. The Aboriginal name (near Cairns) for this Macaranga was 'dugural' or 'dugul'. The bark was used for twine, suckers for fishing spears, and the leaves for wrapping food. It flowers and fruits several times a year, and many birds eat the fruits, which are covered with green, rubbery tentacles. Blush Macaranga occurs in Africa, China and northern Australia, extending from Cape York as far south as Lismore in NSW. It is a weed in Hawaii. The gum from the bark produces a glue; the leaves produce dyes, and when fermented can be made into a drink. It is being used for the production of wood chip and particle board in some parts of the world. It too is a host to the Blue Moonbeam butterfly.

Ht >28m   Lf 40-500x25-445mm   Fl Jun-Mar   Fr Sep-Feb 6-13mm + tentacles

108 Red Kamala

Mallotus philippensis is a small rainforest tree growing on the edge of open forest. The rich orange-red of the berries (Right) attracts attention, but the leaves are interesting, having unequal sides, white underneath, with two glands near the stem junction. The fruits, borne at any time of year, are eaten by Figbirds and Honey-eaters. Red Kamala grows from Cape York to the Hunter R. in NSW and in the NT and PNG. It is found across tropical and temperate Asia, where it is used to produce both red and yellow dyes, and it contains numerous compounds with medicinal value.

Ht >25m Lf 15-210mm Fl Jan-Dec Fr 4-8mm

109 Golden Bouquet Tree

Deplanchea tetraphylla is a tree found in open forest and rainforest, usually in moist situations. The striking flowerheads are the size of dinner plates, rising above the untidy whorls of large hairy leaves. The tree illustrated (Left & Below) was on the coastal spur of Mt. Cook, with branches twisted by the wind. Trees in more sheltered locations can be tall and straight. Young trees grow huge pointed leaves (Below, Centre) in whorls of three, often coloured purple on the underside. The nectar rich flowers attract birds and butterflies, and flying foxes at night, and were eaten as a snack food by Aboriginal people. The timber is rather soft.

Ht >20m   Lf 10-350x55-180mm   Fl Jul-Nov 40-70mm   Fr Nov-Dec 80-110mm

110 Forest Siris

Albizia procera can grow to a large tree, but those found in the open forest are usually a modest size, with a rather smooth, white bark. As this is a deciduous species, the bare white branches can be very obvious, especially along the Cook highway north of Cairns. The crown on these trees is usually rather open (Left) and the leaves are compound. The numerous greenish yellow flowers form pale heads about 24mm in diameter. The fruits are reddish-brown pods (Right), often borne in profusion, once again making the tree quite outstanding.

In North Queensland this tree has some value as cattle food, and was regarded as a sign of good land for sugarcane. It can be seen growing next to sugarcane near Port Douglas. However, it is also found across Southern Asia and has been naturalised in parts of the West Indies, and is an important tree crop. Also known as **Tall Albizia** or **White Siris**, this tree provides a wood used for furniture, carving and boat construction, amongst many other uses. The timber is termite resistant, and has an interlocking grain, with a lovely chocolate brown heartwood, reputed to be rather brittle. It is being considered as a possible source of high quality paper, and also for ethanol production, where it is expected to produce upwards of 10 barrels per hectare. The leaves are insecticidal, but are cooked and eaten as a green vegetable in the Philippines. The bark is a fish poison, and the wood produces a reddish brown gum, while a newly discovered acid, procera acid, is derived from the seeds. Forest Siris grows best in high rainfall areas, but once established is drought (but not frost) tolerant. It is easy to establish and produces sustainable timber yeilds on a 40 year rotation. It coppices vigorously if cut for firewood. Being a legume, it is able to fix nitrogen in poor soils, and has value in revegetating difficult areas. It is also used as a shade tree for tea.

Ht >20m   Lf 15-60mm leaflet   Fl Jan-Mar 8-10mm   Fr Jun-Sep 100-250mm

111 Quinine Tree

Petalostigma pubescens is a shrub or small tree, the undersides of the small rather rounded leaves whitish with fine hairs. It grows mainly in woodland or open forest under Eucalypts, or on coastal sand dunes, and is widespread across northern and eastern Australia and is also found in Papua New Guinea. It is common at the base of Mt Cook. The bark is roughly fissured and old trees develop gnarled trunks. The flowers are cream to fawn, male flowers in clusters of 3 or 4, female flowers solitary. The fruits (Right) are orange with a fleshy and extremely sour exterior, woody inside, and containing 3 or 4 dark brown seeds. The fruits are eaten by emus. Aboriginal people used the fruit, held in the mouth, to ease toothache, and ate them to prevent pregnancy.

Ht >10m   Lf 6-80mm   Fl any month 4-12mm   Fr Jan-Oct 10-25mm

112 Mistletoe Tree

Exocarpus latifolius, also known as the **Broad Leaved Native Cherry**, or **Doughboy**, is a smallish dark foliaged tree (Right). The leaves are fleshy and quite rounded, with almost parallel veins, quite unusual for this leaf shape. The fruits are a green drupe and held in an orange or red fleshy receptacle like an egg in an egg cup (Left). The fruit is reputed to be sweet and palatable when fully ripe, though the foliage may be toxic. Remember that it is most unwise to eat native fruits unless you are confident of their identity. This tree is a root parasite and is difficult to grow without using a suitable plant to which it can attach. Aboriginal people extracted a tonic from the bark that either prevented pregnancy or caused sterilization of the women who drank it. The wood was used for digging sticks. The wood and leaves have mosquito repellent properties.

Ht >10m   Lf 30-140mm   Fl Jan-Jul   Fr Jun-Dec 4-13mm

113 Kapok Tree

Cochlospermum gillivraei is the somewhat tortuous scientific name for this interesting small deciduous tree. The bright yellow flowers appear on the bare branches (Right). As the tree is commonly seen on rocky outcrops, this makes it a striking image in full flower. This tree was near Mt Cook. The leaves are often 5 - 7 lobed, and the fruit is a green, (ripening to brown), pod, which splits (Below) to show the kapok fibres within. The seeds are embedded in the fibres, as with cotton, and have to be removed if the fibre is to be used. The kapok once used in pillows comes from a closely related tree. The wood is soft and fibrous, and the tree commonly has only a few, rather elegantly balanced, branches.

Ht >10m   Lf 50-150mm   Fl Jun-Oct 70-100mm   Fr Oct-Feb 60-95mm

114 Cocky Apple

Planchonia careya is a common understorey tree of open forest throughout Cape York and North Queensland, but in coastal forest it can grow into a substantial tree, with a trunk over 300mm through (Above, Right). The tiny tree (Above, Left) is growing on Mt Cook under other trees, but is also mature enough to flower. The picture (Above, Centre) is of the common small and untidy understory tree showing Autumn colour in an otherwise drab forest. The flowers with pink and white stamens forming a delicate sphere, open at night and fall early, so are not often seen. The fruits are large green berries (Above) which are eaten by Cockatoos.

Ht >15m   Lf 25-150mm   Fl Sep-Nov   Fr Dec-Jan 50-90mm

115 Golden Parrot Tree

Grevillea pteridiifolia grows as a small tree on the beach near Hopevale, but is more common as an inland tree found throughout Cape York. The toothbrush like bunches of yellow to gold flowers (Right & Below) are held on the upper side of the slender branches. The slim trees (Right, Below) have adapted well to the more open areas beside roads, where they are distinguishable by the fine silvery foliage and the delicate spread of the deeply dissected leaves on the branches. The flowers are rich in nectar, attracting Blue-faced Honeyeaters, Rainbow Lorikeets, flying foxes and native bees. Aboriginal people sucked nectar direct from the flowers, or made a sweet drink by soaking them in water. The trees are quick growing and grow well from seed. A prostrate form is known and numerous hybrids have been produced as garden plants.

Ht >14m   Lf 50-250mm leaflet   Fl Apr-Oct   Fr Jul 14-21mm

55

116 White Cedar

Melia azedarach is a rainforest tree commonly found in open forest. The large open compound leaves (Right) are distinctive, though the tree is bare when wintering. The flowers are commonly mauve, but can vary from white to blue to pink. The 15-40mm fruits turn yellow, then orange or brown. Spectacled Flying Foxes and many species of birds eat them. The timber is soft, but quite attractive with broad pink bands in the grain. White Cedar trees in dry inland areas are a sign of previous habitation, as they made good shade trees. The fruit, though, is poisonous to humans and children have died from eating the berries.

Ht >45m Lf 20-70mm Fl Aug-Dec Fr Mar-Jun

117 Pink Poplar

Euroschinus falcata is another rainforest species often found on the margin with open forest. The leaves are smooth and glossy, arranged in pairs in compound leaflets. 'Falcata' means 'sickle shaped' and refers to the shape of the leaflets. Small flowers are followed by mango shaped fruit ripening from green to blue or purple to black. Squashed fruit smell like Mango (no 390) which is a related species. Large trees may have buttresses. The wood is pinkish grey, with yellow streaks, having a fine even texture. As the grain is slightly interlocking, the wood was once used for brake blocks, as well as for interior building use, but it is woolly and difficult to work. Pink Poplar, or **Ribbonwood**, occurs from Jervis Bay in NSW to Cooktown, and the fruits are eaten by many bird species.

Ht >30m   Lf 35-120 leaflet   Fl Sep-Nov   Fr Nov-Feb 7-9mm

118 Mango Bark

Canarium australasicum is a large and rather handsome tree from the rainforest that is quite common in the open forest near Cairns. The bright green foliage makes it stand out from the rather drab trees that surround it. The leaves are compound, arranged along a central stem, and they may be pink or red after the tree has wintered, or shed all its leaves (Right). The white or cream flowers are fragrant. The fruits are the size and shape of an olive, blue-grey to black and can be found on the ground under the tree. The trunk may be buttressed, and separate male and female trees occur. Aboriginal people ate the fruit and used the gum as a glue.

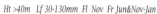

Ht >40m   Lf 30-130mm Fl Nov Fr Jun&Nov-Jan

119 Acacia Cedar

Paraserianthes toona has numerous common names, including **Red Siris** and **Mackay Cedar**. The cabinet timber it produces can cause strong allergic reactions, such as nose bleeds, in timber workers. However it is a beautiful and stable timber. This is another rainforest species commonly found in open forest as a small tree, unlikely to survive a fire. The leaves (Left) are distinctive, with the many tiny leaflets arranged in rows along ribs which are themselves arranged in rows on a central rib. They resemble the leaves of some wattles from southern Australia, hence the 'Acacia' in the common name. The timber is streaked like bacon, with reddish hues that resemble Red Cedar (no 193). Large trees (Right) were once common in rainforest but are now scarce. It is still a relatively common tree in rainforest near Cairns, and is found on Mt. Whitfield. The very fine, dark green, leaves are quite distinctive and make this tree easy to identify from a distance.

Ht >30m   Lf 3-10mm leaflet   Fl Jul-Sep 5-10mm   Fr Sep-Nov 90-160mm

120 Swamp Mahogany

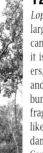

Lophostemon suaveolons is one of the larger trees that make up the open forest canopy. Although the trunk looks rough, it is actually composed of quite soft layers, like tissue paper. The leaves are soft and covered with fine white hairs, and the bunches of white flowers are quite strongly fragrant. The fruits are a capsule, not unlike a gum nut. Swamp Mahogany favours damp, swampy areas, and grows between Cape York and northern NSW, as well as in PNG. It is a host of the Rare Redeye butterfly and the caterpillar of a species of moth tunnels into its stems. Bottlebrush orchids favour its bark, while near Tolga it can be found hosting a beautiful mistletoe. In Cape York it is a favoured nesting tree for the Eclectus Parrot.

Ht >20m   Lf 55-170mm   Fl any month 10mm   Fr Dec 5-8mm wide

121 Foambark

Jagera pseudorhus is a tree that can produce foam in heavy rain, especially after a dry period. It is a medium sized tree with fern like compound leaves often whorled around the ends of branches. It is a hardy garden plant. The unequal sided leaflets are hairy, especially underneath, and have a serrated edge. The white or cream 5 petalled flowers are followed by yellow, orange or brown fruits which are covered with irrititant hairs, and split into 3 segments, each containing one shiny black seed. Numerous birds including Bower Birds eat the fruits. Foambark grows between Cape York and northern NSW, as well as in PNG. The foam comes from Saponin in the leaves and bark, which the Aboriginal people used as a fish poison. It was used as a foaming agent in beer during WW1.

Ht >15m   Lf 25-110mm leaflets   Fl Oct-Jun 4-6mm   Fr Jan-Nov 14-20mm

122 False Gardenia

Atractocarpus sessilis is an attractive shrub or small tree with large glossy leaves and star-like white or cream flowers. The trees are particularly common near Cooktown, though this plant occurs from Cape York to Mareeba near Cairns, and in PNG. It is also known as the **Native Gardenia**. The simple leaves are robust and a dense green. The flowers are fragrant and occur throughout the year, with 4 or 5 petals, often intensely white. The fruits are somewhat elongated, with a cylindrical projection on the end, and on a very short stalk. The surface is sandpapery, and the colour an amorphous pink-purple-brown when ripe. Fruits occur all year and contain several cream seeds.

Ht >15m   Lf 80-240mm   Fl any month 20-40mm   Fr any month 25-60mm

123 Cheese Fruit

Morinda citrifolia bears fruit that stink of rotten cheese. Caassowaries enjoy it. The large leaves with prominent veins grow on square stems. White or cream flowers are followed by the green or creamy yellow fruit (>100mm) containing several seeds. Cheese Fruit grows from Cape York to Mackay, and in the NT, WA, PNG and through Asia and the Pacific. Although it can smell like vomit, the fruit was eaten raw or with salt, or the leaves and seeds eaten. It has many traditional medicinal uses, and Noni juice made from the fruit is a popular alternative medicine, whose benefits are perhaps overstated.

Ht >10m Lf 130-320mm Fl Feb-Nov Fr Mar-Dec

124 Scrub Ebony

Diospyros hebecarpa is related to the ebony that is used in piano keys; the other common name is **Native Persimmon**. "The fruit is deceptive, for it bites and blisters the lips and tongue like caustic, and on being bruised and thrown into a pool on the reef, all fish are killed outright." (E.J. Banfield, Tropic Days) The tree grows separate male and female plants. The leaves are simple, sometimes with sunken glands on the underside. The fragrant flowers vary from white to orange, while the fruit is yellow, orange or pink to red/maroon in colour, with a prominent 3 or 4 lobed calyx. Scrub Ebony occurs from Cape York to Mackay, and through PNG to SE Asia. It is a handsome shrubby tree, containing plumbagin, and the sawdust can cause dermatitis.

Ht >20m   Lf 60-135mm   Fl Jan-Feb 18-20mm   Fr Mar-Dec 25-40mm

125 Bat's Wing Coral Tree

Erythrina vespertilio is a deciduous tree with unusual and distinctive leaves, and colourful flowers. It is widespread across northern and eastern Australia, growing to 30m near Cairns but much less in desert areas. Leaves are comprised of 2 or 3 leaflets of variable shape, but resembling bats in flight. Bright orange to red pea flowers are followed by brown pods (50-150mm) containing red seeds. The pale bark is furrowed and corky and often thorny, and the wood is soft and light. Aboriginal people made necklaces from the seeds, and bowls and shields from the wood.

Ht >30m Lf 20-135mm Fl Apr-Dec Fr Nov-Jul

126 Burdekin Plum

Pleiogynium timorense produces deep red fruits with 'flying saucer' shaped seeds. They make attractive jams and wines, though are too tart to eat raw. (Do not eat native fruits you are not certain of.) The tree can be buttressed, and produces an excellent cabinet timber. Leaflets are composed of 5-11 leaves and the flowers are small and white to yellow-brown. The purple-black fruits (20-28mm) attract Flying Foxes which may spread fruit and stones around the area. While generally too tart to eat, a red and white variety from Townsville is tasty, and Aboriginal people buried the fruits in sand for a few days to improve edibility. The tree grows between Coen and Brisbane, and into SE Asia.

Ht >20m Lf 40-100mm Fl Apr,Jun+Sep-Dec Fr Apr-Oct

127 Coolaroo (Milkwood)

Wrightia saligna is a small tree with narrow bright green leaves that hang downwards from the thin branches. The tree is an open forest species, and puts up suckers some distance from the parent plant. If broken, it exudes a sticky white sap. The leaves have a mid vein with 12 to 18 pairs of side veins. The 5 petalled flower is cream or yellow, and fragrant. The fruits are pods (100-210mm) often in pairs, that open along one side to release numerous seeds with silky white hairs at one end. There are four species of Wrightia in Australia, and Coolaroo is found across northern Australia and down the Queensland coast from Cape York to Marlborough. Allied Rock Wallabies eat the leaves.

Ht >12m Lf 40-190mm Fl Sep-May 8-16mm Fr May-Oct

128 Cape Tamarind

Toechima daemelianum is one of many so-called 'Tamarinds', mostly bearing fruit that divide into three segments. The tree grows compound leaves with 4-11 leaflets with toothed edges. It can be found on Mt Whitfield near Cairns as a small leafy tree that fruits heavily in season. The yellow, orange or red fruits (18-26mm) split in three to reveal dark brown to black seeds, which are eaten by Eclectus Parrots. Metallic Starlings eat the arils which surround the tops of the seeds. Cape Tamarind occurs between Cape York and Tully, and is one of six Australian species of Toechima.

Ht >13m   Lf 45-145mm   Fl Jul-Oct   Fr Sep-Dec

129 Glossy Tamarind

Guoia acutifolia belongs to the same family (Sapindaceae) as the Cape Tamarind (above). Like it, the fruits are three lobed, and split open to reveal the seeds. The tree can be buttressed in rainforest, but is often encountered as a smaller tree or shrub where rainforest is moving into open forest, as occurs on Mt Whitfield near Cairns where these photographs were taken. The leaves on thickened stalks are composed of 2-8 leaflets. The fruits of the Glossy Tamarind can occur in large numbers and are green to pink or reddish capsules with brown seeds enclosed in an orange aril. Yellow Orioles, Silvereyes, and Victoria's Riflebirds eat these seeds. The tree is found between Cape York and SE Qld, and also in PNG.

Ht >20m   Lf 55-200mm leaflets   Fl Mar-Aug   Fr Aug-Feb 10-12mm

130 Brucea

Brucea javanica is the only Australian species from a small family of plants named after James Bruce, who 'found' the Blue Nile. This small tree or shrub has large compound leaves made up of from 3 to 15 toothed leaflets, strongly veined. The small flowers can be white or green to red or purple. The bunches of purplish-black fruit surround the top of the trunk. These fruits were important sources of medicinal compounds in Chinese herbal medicine, used to treat dysentery and malaria. There is now considerable research into the anti-cancer use of the dozen or so compounds isolated from the fruits and stems of this tree. Brucea grows across northern Australia and from Cape York to Mackay, as well as through much of Asia.

Ht >10m   Lf 50-120mm leaflets   Fl Oct-Feb&Jun   Fr Feb-Jul 4-10mm

Coastal Open Forest - Trees

131 Sweet Blackthorn

Bursaria tenuifolia is a shrub or small tree which grows masses of white flowers that attract birds. The tree has rather pendulous thin branches and the leaves taper to the stem, with somewhat rounded ends, and a thin leathery look. The trunk is covered with creamy grey smooth bark. The flowers are fragrant or unpleasantly scented, the five green, white or cream petals interspersed with stamens. The fruits are small purse-like capsules, heartshaped, which split to release several brown seeds. Only six Bursaria species are known, all from Australia. Sweet Blackthorn is found from Iron Range to Mackay. It is grown overseas as a garden plant to attract birds.

Ht >20m   Lf 25-95mm   Fl May-Oct 8-12mm   Fr Aug-Dec 6-8mm

132 Corkwood (Butterfly Plant)

Carallia brachiata is the only Australian species of Carallia. The pale corky bark is the outstanding feature of this tree, photographed in the Cooktown Botanic Gardens. It is also known as **Corky Bark**. The Corkwood tree favours areas close to the sea or rivers, though in Asia it can grow in upland rainforest. The simple leaves are

oval, the undersides dotted with black or brown glands. The small green, white or cream flowers are followed by orange, pink, red or black berries eaten by many birds, including the Torresian Imperial Pigeon. It is the host to the Peacock Jewel and Four O'clock Moths, as well as two butterflies. Corkwood occurs from Cape York to Rockhampton; also northern Australia, the Solomon Islands, SE Asia, and Madagascar.

Ht >30m   Lf 50-160mm   Fl Jul-Sep
Fr Sep-Nov 7-10mm

133 Weeping Cleistanthus

Cleistanthus apodus is a small tree or shrub with attractive weeping foliage and plentiful three valved fruit. The tree carries long drooping branches with simple elongated leaves arranged on each side. The small green, white or cream flowers are followed by green to brown three lobed fruit, carried above the branches.

There are nine species of Cleistanthus in Australia, and the Weeping Cleistanthus occurs from Cape York to the Herbert River, and is also found in PNG.

Since this tree thrives on the edge of rainforest, it has found favour as an edge plant in gardens throughout Australia, helped by its soft pink new growth.

Ht >12m   Lf 18-195mm   Fl Sep-Feb   Fr Sep-Apr 7-10mm

134 Hakea

Hakea pedunculata is a small tree with radiating dull green leaves at the tips of thin branches. The leaves taper to the stem, but are quite pointed at the tip.

The flowers form a loose ball of white blossom on a peduncle, or stem, from which comes the 'pedunculata' of the scientific name. Flowering is in spring, and the fruits which follow are elongated woody capsules, grey brown in colour, which eventually open wide to release the seeds.

This hakea is one of many Australian species, and is found in Cape York as far south as Cooktown. The flower in the photograph came from Keating's Lagoon. The species was first collected in 1770 by the botanists with Cook on the 'Endeavour'.

135 Harvey's Buttonwood (Butterfly Plant)

Glochidion harveyanum is a small tree or srub which grows striking fruit along thin branches. The tree grows in open forest and in rainforest between Cooktown and Proserpine. The leaves are densely arranged along the branches, with short stalks. Flowers lack petals, and the green, white or yellow sepals can be seen in any month. The fruits are enclosed in a white

to pink capsule which falls away to reveal the seeds which are covered in a yellow, orange or red aril. These fruits attract many species of birds.

Harvey's Buttonwood is one of about 15 Australian species of Glochidion, and occurs between Cooktown and Proserpine, as well as in the NT and PNG. It is a host tree for the Miskin's Jewel butterfly, and is used in streambank revegetation.
Ht >12m   Lf 40-190mm   Fl any month 5mm   Fr Jun-Feb 8x12-18mm

136 Hop Bush

Dodonea polyandra is a tree that can reach 8 metres in height, though most of its 60 relatives in Australia are shrubs. The leaves can be somewhat sticky due to resin dots on both surfaces. They taper to a short stalk. Small yellow or green flowers can be found at any time of year, while the fruits are 2 or 3 winged capsules which are yellow-green with purple wings when young, ripening to brown.

Hop Bush occurs throughout Cape York south to Cooktown, and it is one of the dominant sub-canopy trees in some sandy areas. It is also found in PNG. The tree at right was growing in the Cooktown Botanic Gardens.
Ht >8m   Lf 55-125mm   Fl any month 5mm   Fr May-Nov 16-28mm

Coastal Open Forest - Palms

137 Northern Cabbage Tree Palm

Livistona muelleri is a palm with broad, almost circular fronds, with the leaf segments free for about half their length. It is found through forested areas from Cape York to Innisfail. There is a small population at Taylor Point near Cairns. The fronds grow on stems over a metre long, which are armed with sharp hooks along the edges near the base. Flowers are cream to yellow, and are borne on a metre long panicle, with blue-black or black fruit following. These fruits are eaten by Pied Imperial Pigeons. This species has been sold around the world for garden use, but is slow to establish and requires full sun. The name 'cabbage tree' is associated with woven palm hats, made by the early settlers in Australia, from leaves of related species .

Ht >18m   Lf 70-1300mm   Fl Jun-Jul   Fr Sep-Dec 10-12mm

138 Kennedy Palm

Photo
Norm Scott

Corypha utan is a spectacular palm from Cape York that is found on the low grassy plains of Lakefield National Park, west of Cooktown. These big palms reach 25 metres in height, out-topping almost everything around them. The fan shaped leaves on spiny stems can reach 7 metres in length. Younger trees, such as the one in the middle of the three below, tend to retain dead fronds. As the tree grows, these are shed and the trunk is revealed with a spiral pattern of scars where leaves had previously attached. After 40 to 50 years, the mature tree is ready to produce fruit. A huge terminal flower head develops, the largest in the plant kingdom, 3 to 4 metres in height (Left). It bears up to a million small creamy white flowers, and over the next 18 months the fruits ripen from olive green to almost black. Each fruit contains one seed, and 500-800kg of fruit can be produced by one palm. Seeding finished, the palm dies. The palm on the left below has already seeded. In Australia these palms occur in an area on the East Coast of Cape York, north-west of Cooktown, and another area on the Mitchell River near Kowanyama on the west coast, with some smaller occurrances further north. They also occur in the NT, and through PNG to the Pacific and Asia. Aboriginal people ate the flesh of the seeds, and used the leaves for shelter. In Asia the leaves were plaited into containers. The fruits are eaten by figbirds and feral pigs.

Ht >25m   Lf 2-5.4m   Fl Aug-Oct 5-8mm (inflorescence 3-4m)   Fr any month 20-30mm

139 Palm Cycad (Primitive Plant)

Cycas media is common in open forest. It is a modern representaive of the Gymnosperms, which first appeared about 245 million years ago, and became a dominant form of vegetation in the Jurassic period. Cycads are unusual in having mobile swimming sperm and require water for fertilisation to occur. Male and female plants are separate, with fronds up to 2 metres long, on stems to 6 metres. The photo (Below, Left) shows a plant with a male cone, while that (Right) shows a female cone, with the fruit emerging. The large seeds (Centre) are extremely toxic to humans but are eaten by Cassowaries. The somewhat similar Zamia Palm (no 198) is also a cycad. Growing in rainforest, it gets much taller, with longer fronds.

140 Native Lasiandra

Melastoma malabathricum is an attractive flowering shrub which occurs in open forest as well as disturbed areas of rainforest. Lasiandra is a purple flowered garden plant, and the common name points to the similarity of the flowers of these two species. The flowers of the Native Lasiandra can be purple or white, usually with 5 petals. The dark green leaves are hairy and 3-5 veined (Below). The plant commonly grows 1-2 metres in height, but can reach 3 metres. The fruits were eaten by Aboriginal people, and stain the mouth blue, hence the common name **Blue Tongue**. This plant is widely distributed around the Indian and Pacific oceans. Do not risk eating native fruits unless you are sure of their identity.

141 Lantana (Major Weed)

Lantana camara grows beautiful flowers in shades ranging from white to vivid yellows, reds and pinks, often blended in the same flower head. It is also one of Australia's worst weeds, having spread over much of the eastern coast and hinterland since its introduction from tropical America. The long scrambling stems are covered in prickles, and the small shiny black fruit are eaten by many birds which spread seeds across the countryside. The plant is poisonous to stock, and the unripe fruit are particularly poisonous to humans, and can be fatal. The photographs show some of the colour variations.

142 Potato Bush

Solanum sp. (Font Hills) *(syn. intonsum)* is one of about 30 Solanums growing in the Wet Tropics area in North Queensland. This is one of the native species, with plants to 2 metres. The flowers are blue/purple, while the fruits are yellow-green to green when ripe. Potato Bush is found in open forest, as well as on the margins of rainforest. Many of the solanum species in the North are common along the margins of rainforest. This species has no prickles on the softly hairy leaves and usually none on the typically straight branches. More distant introduced relatives include tobacco, tomatoes and potatoes. Within the family are a number of poisonous plants such as the nightshades, as well as a number of edible plants. The potato (for example) has poisonous fruits, but edible tubers. The toxicity of many of these plants remains untested.

Ht >2m   Lf c100-150mm   Fl 20mm   Fr >16mm

143 Devil's Fig (Weed)

Solanum torvum is a native of the West Indies that grows on the edges of rainforest and in nearby open forest. The leaves are thickly covered with star like radiating hairs, which causes them to feel soft, similar to flannel. The flowers are white, green or cream. The name would suggest it is toxic, but the edibility of a number of these species is not known. The leaves of many Solanums are vary variable, either simple, or somewhat lobed, or deeply lobed, with perhaps a mixture on one plant. This plant carries 8mm hooked thorns on the stems, while many Solanums have straight spines on stems and even leaves. Again this can vary from plant to plant within a species.

Ht >4m   Lf 55-220mm   Fl any month 20-25mm   Fr any month 10-15mm

144 Wild Tobacco (Major Weed)

Solanum mauritianum is an imported weed, coming originally from Argentina. This robust shrub is now found from Cairns to Sydney. In North Queensland the fruit is favoured by the Brown Cuckoo-Dove, a large brown pigeon, which is widely credited with spreading the seeds. However, many other birds enjoy feeding on the fruit of this plant. The large leaves (Right) appear silver due to their covering of fine hairs. Where the leaf stalk meets the stem is a pair of stipules that look like smaller leaflets. The flowers are blue or purple, while the fruit are green, yellow or brown. The plant contains valuable steroids, but all parts are poisonous to us.

Ht >4m   Lf 125-330mm   Fl any month 15-25mm   Fr any month 12-18mm

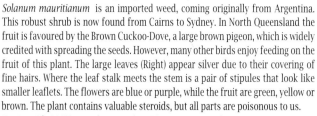

Coastal Open Forest - Shrubs

145 Coffee Bush (Butterfly Plant)

Breynia oblongifolia is a shrub which bears bright red berries above graceful branches. The leaves are oval and bright green, or whitish (Right). Small green, white or red flowers at any time produce orange, pink, red or black berries which can be ribbed, and are eaten by Brown Cuckoo Doves. Coffee Bush is found from Cape York to south of Sydney, also in the NT and Melanesia. It is the host plant to several butterflies and moths, including the Common Grass Yellow butterfly.

Ht >8m   Lf 8-30mm   Fl any month 2-3mm   Fr any month 5-10mm

146 White Currant

Flueggea virosa is a shrub which produces bunches of snowy white fruits on stems which bear alternating leaves. The shrub can reach a height of 5 metres, and is deciduous, with male and female plants. The leaves are simple, but can be toothed. The small fragrant flowers are composed of 5 green, white or yellow sepals, without petals. The fruits are borne at any time of year and are the most striking feature of the plant, due to their extreme whiteness. They are 3 to 8mm across, containing 6 white or brown seeds, and are eaten by Yellow-spotted Honeyeaters and Helmeted Friarbirds. Another common name for this plant is **Snowball Bush**. White Currant is found across northern Australia, and from Cape York to Marlborough. It also occurs in PNG, Indonesia and Africa, where it is widespread. Aboriginal people ate the fruits, drank an infusion for stomach pain, and rubbed it on the skin for treating skin diseases. The stems made good fire sticks. In Africa a host of medicinal uses were known, including treatment of sleeping sickness. The bark was used as a fish poison. The main active ingredient is bergenin.

Ht >5m   Lf 15-125mm   Fl Apr-Feb   Fr Nov-Jun 2-7mm

147 Smell of the Bush

Mallotus claoxyloides is a shrub which has an odour to which some people are very sensitive, and variously described as a forest fragrance, earthy, and smelling of possums. In the Cooktown Botanic gardens it is one of the most asked about plants.

Smell of the Bush grows opposed leaves often unequal in size, hairy, and commonly toothed. The small yellow, green or white flowers produce 2-3 valved fruits which are hairy capsules, turning brown.

Also known as **Green Kamala**, this bush occurs from Cape York to the Richmond River in NSW, also in PNG, often on the edges of dry rainforest.

Ht >8m   Lf 35-170mm   Fl Aug-Apr   Fr Nov-Aug

Coastal Open Forest - Shrubs

148 Guinea Flower

Hibbertia melhanioides is a shrub of open forest that grows showy bright yellow blossoms throughout the year. This plant was growing near Cardwell.

The bush grows thin stems that may be reddish. The leaves are simple and surround the stems. On top they are clothed with star-like hairs, that give them a sandpapery feel, while the pale star-like hairs under the leaves make them appear whitish in colour. The leaf stalks are very short. The yellow flowers with 5 petals can be found throughout the year. The fruit is a small capsule enclosing two cream or brown seeds, each of which is wrapped in a cream or white aril.

This is one of about 100 Australian species of Hibbertia, and is found only between Iron Range and Paluma, usually in open forest or along rainforest margins.

Ht >1.5m   Lf 12-55mm   Fl any month 10-18mm   Fr Nov 3mm

149 Pinkburr (Weed)

Urena lobata is a widespread weed with attractive pink Hibiscus-like flowers, atop an untidy shrubby bush. This is a shrub that often develops reddish stems. The leaves can be lobed, with from 3 to 9 lobes, or unlobed. They are covered with raspy star-like hairs, giving them a felt-like appearance, the underside often whitish. The leaf stalks, which are thickened at both ends, can be up to 120mm in length. The pink or purple flowers are about 40mm across. The green to brown seed pods are clothed with hooked bristles, and contain 5 seeds. The burrs readily attach to clothing. Pinkburr is an introduced weed that has naturalised between Cape York and Buderim, especially in pastures. It probably originated in Asia, but is now found world wide. It is cultivated in Brazil and the Congo to produce a strong and lustrous fibre used in sacking and twine. The leaves and flowers are eaten in famine. Extracts from the leaves and roots are used in herbal medicine to treat many ailments, and the root extract has been shown to have good antibacterial properties.

Ht >2.5m   Lf 20-90x20-100mm   Fl Apr-Oct >40mm   Fr Apr-Oct 8mm

150 Bush Hibiscus

Hibiscus meraukensis is an attractive native hibiscus with thin foliage and large but drooping flowers. It grows as a shrub of woodlands in tropical Australia. The leaves are quite variable, either lobed (with 3-5 lobes) or unlobed, and often with hooks along the veins. The stems can also be spiny. The leaf edges are toothed, and the surface can be sandpapery. The flowers are white, cream or pink, with a maroon or purple centre. A cultivar with reddish flowers is being sold under the name "State of Origin". This is an annual plant, appearing during the wet season and dying off in the dry season. Flowers last only a couple of days but are quickly replaced. This plant occurs across northern Australia north of Townsville, as well as in PNG. The flowers are edible, but the plant may cause dermatitis.

Ht > 3m   Lf 30-180x30-180mm   Fl Dec-Sep >90mm   Fr Feb-Sep 8-17mm

151 Small Passionfruit (Weed)

Passiflora suberosa comes originally from South America, but is now naturalised throughout much of coastal Queensland. This is a climbing vine, corky at the base, with fine tendrils with which it clings to other vegetation. The leaves can be simple (Left) or lobed (Right) and there are two tiny black glands on the middle of the leaf stalk. The leaves may change in waves as the plant grows and ages. The greenish yellow star-like flower has no petals, and the blue/black fruit are only about 10mm across. The fruits are eaten by King Parrots and Cuckoo Doves. Small passionfruit has become an aggressive weed across many South Pacific islands. It can be found on Forgon Smith Spur in open forest near Cairns and also inland near Davies Ck.

Lf 20-100x12-100mm   Fl Feb-Oct 8-30mm   Fr Feb-Oct 6-15mm

152 Stinking Passion Flower (Weed)

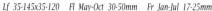

Passiflora foetida is a native of South America now widely naturalised throughout coastal Queensland. Despite the name, which refers to the smell of the crushed leaves, it is an attractive vine with clear white or purple flowers (Right) with fruit that are orange when ripe (Left), enclosed by three lacy bracts. These bracts can trap insects, and it may be that the vine is carnivorous. They also give rise to another common name, **Love-in-a-mist**. The vine has thin tendrils which allow it to climb over low vegetation. Stinking Passion Flower is now a weed throughout the tropics, invasive on many Pacific islands. It produces a tanning agent used in parts of Asia. The seeds are dispersed by many birds and mammals. Cape York Aboriginal people ate the fruits, which contain a small quantity of sweetly tart pulp.

Lf 35-145x35-120   Fl May-Oct 30-50mm   Fr Jan-Jul 17-25mm

153 Native Jasmine

Jasminum elongatum is a scrambling vine which can be found in open forest near to rainforest. It also grows in rainforest near the coast. The shiny leaves taper to a point, and there is a joint half way along the leaf stalk. The flowers have a beautiful fragrance. The number of petals is variable, between five and eight. The purple or black berries are eaten by

Metallic Starlings. Native Jasmine is now a common sight in gardens as well as in the wild, grown both for the attractive star-like flowers and for the perfume it produces.

Native Jasmine is found across much of Asia and into the northern part of Australia, from Townsville to Cape York and also in the NT and WA. The flowers of this or similar species are used to flavour tea and also dishes such as rice, particularly in China. There are a number of other plants which are also known as Native Jasmine in Australia.

Lf 30-120mm   Fl Jul-Nov 12-32mm   Fr Aug-Mar 7-11mm

154 Wonga Wonga Vine

Pandorea pandorana is a scrambling vine that can bloom at any time of year, but is commonly seen in the dry season months of Aug-Oct. The white or cream flowers have pink and purple markings in their throats, and are held in drooping sprays above the vine. There are many varied colours and forms of these flowers, ranging to yellow and brown. The flowers are scented. The leaves are compound, with from 3 to 15 leaflets on a stem, each rounded with an extended point. Young leaves can be fern like. This vine is easy to grow, and can be an attractive garden plant. Some

varieties have been given horticultural names, such as the yellow variety 'Golden Showers'. The plants are tolerant of shade and frost. Wonga Wonga vine is found from Cape York to Bass Strait, across N Australia, and into SE Asia.

Lf 20-140mm   Fl any month 10-32mm
Fr Sep-Mar 40-120mm

155 Chain Fruit

Alyxia spicata is a shrubby vine, that scrambles over rocks or other vegetation by means of long shoots that find some purchase on nearby objects. It is tough and elastic, and when growing in thick clumps is hard to walk through. Unlike the Alyxias that grow in rainforest, the leaves are not prickly, though they are pointed. The sap is white and sticky. The small 5-petalled flowers can be green, white, or yellow, with a fragrant smell. The fruit (Right & Left) can be single or in pairs, like

beads on a chain. They ripen to yellow, orange or black. These plants can be found in open bush or in vine thickets, especially along watercourses. They are found in tropical Australia and in PNG. Joseph Banks and his party collected the first specimens near the Endeavour River in 1770.

Lf 30-110mm Fl Jun-Jan Fr any month 7-16mm

156 Suppplejack

Flagellaria indica is a long woody vine with stems up to 30mm thick, with a slight resemblance to Lawyer Cane. The long leaves with whip like tendrils at the ends are attached alternately along the stem, which rarely branches. Another name is **Whip Vine**. The vine is able to climb into the forest canopy using these tendrils to grasp other plants. The small, white, fragrant flowers grow in a bunch at the vine's tip and are followed by grape like bunches of pink or reddish fruit. Supplejack grows in rainforest or nearby open forest or watercourses, from Sydney north and across tropical Australia. It is also found in PNG, the Pacific Islands, SE Asia, India and Africa. Aboriginal people ate the fruit and had many uses for the plant. It made a strong rope for climbing and the stems were woven into fish and eel traps or used to sew together bark canoes. The sap from the tip was applied to sore eyes and used as a contraceptive, as well as being used to heal wounds.

Ht >10m   Lf 60-400mm   Fl Jun-Dec   Fr Nov-Apr 5-8mm

157 Velvet Silkpod (Butterfly Plant)

Parsonsia velutina is a twining vine of open forest and rainforest edges that is notable for the velvety hairs on the leaves, stems and pods. It grows on Mt. Cook and near Hartley's Creek. This vine occurs from northern NSW across tropical Australia to WA. The stem is woody, reaching lengths of 8 metres, and the leaves are pointed with softly hairy undersides. The flowers (Left) are white, cream, yellow or brown, fragrant, and occur in any month. The fruits are green to brown capsules, usually in pairs, which split to release numerous seeds attached to brown plumes.

Velvet Silkpod is a host plant for butterflies, including the Common Crow. The plant contains alkaloids, including pyrrolizidine.

Lf 30-190mm   Fl any month 3-6mm   Fr Dec-Aug 70-160mm

158 Scarlet Creeper (Weed)

Ipomoea hederifolia is an introduced weed with attractive small scarlet flowers, and the alternative name of **Cardinal's Flower**. It is a twining vine which can grow 10 metres into trees, but is commonly found in cane fields and on waste ground and disturbed sites. Originating in Central America, it is now widespread throughout the tropics, including Queensland and the Pacific Islands, where dense infestations occur. The leaves are extremely variable, either deeply 3 - 7 lobed (Right) or heart shaped (Left). The flower often has a yellow throat, and the fruit is a capsule containing a few seeds. The root is used medicinally. This plant is common in North Queensland, and can be found on Grassy Hill at Cooktown and near the Bloomfield River. It was a problem weed when cane was cut by hand, as it entangled the sugarcane stalks.

Lf 40-160mm   Fl Mar-Oct 15-25mm   Fr Mar-Oct 6-7mm

159 Sweet Sarsaparilla

Smilax glyciphylla is one of six species of Smilax found in North Queensland, mostly with spiny stems. The stems of Sweet Sarsaparilla are smooth, though, climbing with tendrils that are attached near the leaf stalks. The greenish white flowers occur throughout the year and are followed by dark red or black berries that are eaten by birds and possums. Plants are either male or female. The leaves have three distinct veins and are whitish underneath. Aboriginal people used a tea made from the leaves to cure stomach ache. Early in white settlement of Australia, the leaves of this plant became popular as a tea substitute and diuretic medicine. Nowadays alternative health practitioners are exploring the antioxidant properties of this vine in detoxification rituals.

Ht >5m   Lf 40-100mm   Fl any month 3-4mm   Fr Jan-Sep 6-12mm

Coastal Open Forest - Vines

160 Wombat Berry

Eustrephus latifolius is a scrambling vine with orange fruits on wiry stems. The vine twines and scrambles over other vegetation. The grass like leaves are shiny, terminating in a sharp point, and grow on short stalks. The veins are parallel. The white, purple or pink flowers produce 3 valved fruit with black seeds throughout the year.

Wombat Berry is the single species in its genus. It occurs in shaded areas in open forest from Cape York to Victoria. It is also found in PNG and into SE Asia and the Pacific Islands. The fruits are reputed to be edible, as are the roots which bear small, juicy and sweet tubers. Never eat fruits that you are unsure of.

Lf 25-130mm   Fl Aug-Jun 10-18mm   Fr any month 10-20mm

161 Palmate Morning Glory

Ipomoea mauritiana is a luxurient vine that twines over other vegetation, smothering it with large deeply lobed leaves and pink or purple blossoms. The smooth shiny leaves are 5-7 lobed, on stalks 20-100mm long. The flowers are pinkish-white, pink-red or purple, with a darker throat. The fruits are brown capsules containing 4 brown seeds clothed in woolly hairs. The roots produce tubers up to

300mm long. Palmate Morning Glory probably originated in South America, but it is now widespread around the world. In Australia it occurs from Cape York to Mackay, also in the NT. In China the leaves and roots are used to treat TB and it has many uses in Indian herbal medicine, including its use as a medicinal wine.

*Lf 60-180x80-200mm   Fl Sep-May 60-80mm
Fr Feb-Dec 9-14mm*

162 Butterfly Pea, Centro (Weed)

Centrosema molle (prev. Centrosema pubescens) is a twining vine of coastal areas, introduced as a cattle fodder crop and now widespread. The compound leaves are made up of three slightly to very hairy leaflets typically dark green when mature. The pale to bright lilac flowers have a cream centre with some darker markings. The pods are long and thin and contain up to 20 brown and black seeds.

Centro originated in South America, where there are about 50 related species. It has been spread around the wet tropics as a cover crop and cattle pasture. In Queensland it is found from Iron Range to the SE corner of the state. It is an invasive weed in the Pacific islands and in cane here.

Lf 13-105mm   Fl May-Sep   Fr Apr-Sep 40-150mm

Coastal Open Forest - Orchids

While orchids are common in rainforest, they are not often seen flowering, since they are usually in the canopy where they can find light. In open forest there are a number of species which are common, sometimes in great numbers, with most of these flowering in the drier months (Aug-Oct). Orchids are considered the most highly evolved form of flowering plants and can be incredibly diverse. Sadly, their numbers have been greatly reduced in many areas through over-collecting and the beautiful Cooktown Orchid, Queensland's floral emblem, is now quite rare near Cooktown and unlikely to be seen in the wild. (Photo Left: John Lang Photography) However there are still areas where the orchids below are abundant. Please admire them and leave them alone.

163 Pencil Orchid

Dockrillia teretifolia (Prev. Dendrobium teretifolium) is a common orchid, easily distinguished by its long pencil like leaves that hang from the rhizome that attaches to the bark of a suitable tree or a rock face. Trees that regularly shed their bark will not generally host orchids. The flowers are cream to white with thin petals that form a lacy veil over the top of the plant. The root system is whitish and is often quite large. It is common to see more than one colony of these orchids in one tree. They thrive in a variety of habitats, including mangroves, open forest and rainforest. Flowering occurs in the latter part of the year, and is generally over by December.

164 Antelope Orchid

Cepobacalum semifuscum (Prev. Dendrobium semifuscum) grows thin sprays of delicate flowers (Close view, Left) in paperbark trees next to mangroves. It was once very common close to the cemetery in Cooktown but over-collecting has made it more difficult to find. It resembles the Golden Orchid (no 28) though smaller and lighter. The colour varies from a light yellow to deep brown. In less accessible areas it may still be found in large numbers, sometimes close to the ground, and often associated with Ant Plants (no 24).

Many of the orchids previously known as Dendrobium orchids have recently been renamed. Name changes occur because of new knowledge, or through discovering that an earlier name had been overlooked, and is now given priority.

165 Bottlebrush Orchid

Cepobacalum smillieae, the Bottlebrush Orchid, can be found near Daintree Village growing on the papery bark of Swamp Mahogany trees. As this bark is not shed, the roots of the orchids are able to penetrate between the bark layers where they form large, well protected mats. They prefer trees that are exposed to sunlight, like that shown (Left). The brush shaped mass of pink and cream flowers, with greenish tips, is most attractive (Sep-Oct).

166 Tea Tree Orchid

Cepobacalum canaliculatum is known as the Tea Tree Orchid because it prefers the type of paperbark tree commonly known as Tea Tree. As Tea Trees often favour swampy areas, this orchid is likely to be found on the coast close to swamps. The photograph (Left) shows the cream to white flowers held in delicate sprays only about 400mm long. In this case the orchid is growing on the trunk of a coconut tree, indicating it may have been 'planted' there. The thick leaves are deeply channelled on the upper surface and arise from onion-like pseudobulbs, hence the name **Onion Orchid**. The plants can be very numerous in locations they favour, with several on one tree, but their numbers in some areas have been sadly depleted by collecting, or by loss of habitat, particularly to cane growing and now to tourist development. The close-up photograph of flowers (Above, Right) was from the Annan River, near Cooktown.

167 Buttercup Orchid

Cymbibium madidum is a hardy orchid that thrives in open woodland. It favours trees with persistant bark, such as the Baker's Oak, (Left) with its rough corky bark, but can also be found in Eucalypts.

The flowers (Left) are a greenish yellow hanging cup, while the fruits (Below) are ribbed pods. The thickened leaves help store moisture. The flowers are scented and the pseudobulbs were once chewed to treat dysentery. Orchid growers pay very close attention to the amount of light, and particularly water, that is provided to orchid plants. Using the correct medium will help prevent waterlogging.

168 Red Natal Grass (Weed)

Melinis repens can appear striking when lit by the pink light of dawn (Right). It is a grass that originated in Africa, now common along roadsides and on waste ground in North Queensland.

The grass is soft, with fluffy pink seedheads turning paler as they age (Left), and usually below a metre in height. The leaves are from 75 to 150mm long, 3 to 4mm wide, tapering to the tip. The erect seed heads are often partly enclosed by the upper leaf-sheath. The seeds strip easily from the stalk.

Considered a weed, the grass is edible by stock but of little feed value. However it is easily killed by cultivation or eliminated in well managed pasture.

169 Guinea Grass (Weed)

Panicum maximum is everywhere in North Queensland. Introduced from Africa, it can smother most other grasses. Because it can grow under shade, and is very resistant to fire, it can form large masses of vegetation that then burn fiercely, killing those native species that are adapted to cooler fires.

Guinea Grass can grow to 3.5 metres, commonly to 2 metres. It is an erect large-tufted perennial grass, with hairy leaf stalks and leaves from 150 to 1000mm long. The seed is borne on clusters of spikelets, inclined to shatter on harvest. It is a useful stock-feed, and probably for this reason has not been declared a weed in Queensland, where "Green Panic" is a widely grown pasture variety, also used for silage. Guinea Grass is the most productive pasture grass in tropical America, yet it is also a major invasive weed in many parts of the world.

170 Kangaroo Grass

Themeda triandra is a native Australian grass that grows across the whole country. It has distinctive seed heads, and is probably a grass of tropical origin that has adjusted to cooler climates. It forms tussocks which can have a slightly pinkish colour (Left), and in autumn the distinctive seed heads (Right) turn a beautiful golden bronze. While it can be grazed, it is eliminated by over grazing. It is still common throughout North Queensland and can be seen in open forest in many places such as on the ridge near Clifton Beach or the Forgon Smith spur near Paradise Palms golf course.

Closely related to Grader Grass (no 172) it is finer and shorter, commonly less than a metre in height.

Coastal Open Forest - Grasses

171 Molasses Grass (Weed)

Melinis minutiflora is an all-too-common grass in open forest where it has taken over large areas of native grassland. It comes from tropical Africa and has been grown as a pasture grass in countries with moist tropical climates, including Northern Australia.

Molasses grass is a tufted, leafy perennial with loose trailing stems, bearing short flat leaves which are covered in hairs (Right) that secrete a sticky liquid with a strong molasses odour. Since it will grow on poorer soils and it produces vigorous seedlings, it easily becomes the dominant grass and can replace native grasses such as Kangaroo Grass (no 170). The seed heads are a purple/brown colour (Left).

172 Grader Grass (Weed)

Themeda quadrivalvis is a widespread weed of roadsides and overgrazed pasture in Far North Queensland. It is an annual grass with robust clumps (450-1500mm high) the leaf blades from 100 to 300mm long. It develops a characteristic orange to red colour (Left) as it flowers and sets seed. The seeds are large, so can be spread by clothing or on the fur of animals. However they are usually moved by machinery, including graders, which spread them along roadsides.

Grader Grass is a weed of sugar cane, legumes and pastures. It invades degraded native pasture and can reduce diversity, and has been declared a noxious weed in the Northern Territory. It probably originated in India, where it is sometimes used for thatch. It favours sandy loam soils and can withstand dry periods and light frost.

173 Blady Grass (Weed)

Most Australians would be surprised to know that *Imperata cylindrica* is considered the world's tenth worst weed, and possibly the very worst in SE Asia. It is a native of the Philippines, China and Japan (where a red tipped form occurs), and spreads by roots called rhizomes, as well as by seed, with up to 3000 tiny but fertile seeds produced by a single seed head. Leaves are usually over a metre long, hairy near the base, with silica crystals along the leaf margins. The seed head is a soft, silvery, plume-like spike. The grass burns hot, destroying nearby vegetation, but quickly recovers from the deep rhizomes, and even increases in strength. Blady grass can dramatically reduce production of crops like corn, its roots competing for nutrients as well as suppressing the growth of nearby plants. Australian wattles are now being used to regenerate land lost to Blady Grass in Indonesia.

174 Cardwell Lily

Proiphys amboinensis is a native lily which grows new, almost circular, leaves as the wet season arrives, quickly followed by the beautiful white scented flowers with a yellow throat. Flowering is followed by green to blackish 25-30mm capsules (Left), which often ripen on the plant. (Proiphys means 'bring forth early'.) It is sometimes known as **Christmas Lily**, due to the flowering period beginning at Christmas. During the dry season the leaves die away. Cardwell Lily prefers open forest bordering rainforest or lightly shaded rainforest. It is found from Central Queensland to Cape York, also WA, and extends into Indonesia and SE Asia.

Ht >1m Lf 200-350mm Fl Dec-Apr 25-40mm Fr Jan-May

175 River Lily

Crinum pedunculatum has numerous common names, including **Swamp Lily** and **Mangrove Lily**. It is found from Northern NSW through coastal Queensland, and through PNG to the Pacific Islands. As the names imply, this is a lily of wet areas, including the high tide level in mangroves. The River Lily is a large bulbous perennial herb, with straplike leaves up to 2 metres long and 150mm wide, terminating in blunt points. The plant can reach 2-3 metres in height, with a spread of up to 3 metres. Flowers are borne in a cluster with from 10 to as many as 100 flowers on an umbel. The flowers are white (Right) and fragrant. The fruit are the size of small onions, also white, and may germinate while still on the plant. This plant has been used for street plantings in Sydney and elsewhere. The sap was used as an antidote to marine stingers.

Ht >3m   Lf 50-2000x50-150mm   Fl Oct-Feb 80-110mm   Fr Dec-Feb 30-50mm

176 Onion Lily (Field Lily)

Crinum angustifolium is a lily of the Eastern slopes of Queensland's coastal ranges, and is also found in the Northern Territory and northern WA. Like the River Lily (Above) it likes plenty of moisture, growing on coastal flats that are often inundated in the wet season, or in brackish areas close to mangroves. The plant (Right) was growing at Keating's Lagoon, near Cooktown. The Onion Lily is smaller and less robust than the related River Lily and the flowers have narrower petals and are upright when young. Their fragrance attracts bees, butterflies and birds. The Crinum family originated in Africa, and spread to Australia via Asia and Indonesia. While the River Lily probably arrived via PNG, the Onion Lily possibly was introduced from Timor, spreading across central Australia in a wetter period than now, so that many forms have developed where they have crossed the Eastern ranges. It is listed as a poisonous plant and was used by Aboriginal people as a linament, an analgesic and a dressing for wounds.

Ht >1m   Fl Oct-Feb

177 Cape York Lily

Curcuma australasica is not a lily, despite the common name, but belongs to the same family as the Gingers. It blooms at the beginning of the wet season, and is one of the most attractive Cape York plants. The leaves are pleated and shiny, eventually out-topping the earlier separate flower stalk. The flowers proper are yellow, with 3 petals, but the surrounding bracts are pink, red or mauve, though green near the base. The fruit is a capsule within pink or purplish bracts. Cape York Lily occurs from Cape York to Cooktown and also is found in the NT and PNG. The variety "Aussie Plume" grows to 6' in the US. The long lasting cut flowers are now grown in Zimbabwe. Aboriginees ate the tubers roasted.

Ht >500mm Lf 140-450mm Fl Nov-Mar Fr Feb-Mar

178 Musk Mallow

Abelmoschus moschatus is a striking plant due to the intensity of its rich pink flowers. It belongs to the same family as Hibiscus, closely related to Okra, and is sometimes called the **Native Rosella**. Musk Mallow grows across Northern Australia, and from Cape York to SE Qld, in open forest, usually as a rather small trailing plant with hairy stems, rarely exceeding 1 metre in height. It appears during the wet season, flowering after the first rains, and then dying away to its edible underground tuber, thick and carrot-like, during the dry season. Aboriginal people ate the leaves and the tubers. The black seeds are held in tough, papery capsules. The leaves are usually lobed (Right), but can vary greatly. In India it is grown for its medicinal properties and also to produce Ambrette Oil, valued for its musky odour. Occasionally white flowered specimens are found. This could be an attractive garden plant, though the flowers do not last long. It has become a weed on some Pacific islands.

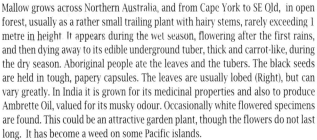

Ht >1m Lf 40-100mm Fl Oct-Apr

179 Brahmin Ginseng (Curculigo)

Curculigo orchioides (prev ensifolia) is a small lily-like plant about 300-400mm high, which grows bright yellow flowers from the base. Underground there is a tuber, an elongated corm (>9x160mm), which is important in chinese medicine. It is used as a tonic and aphrodisiac, and particularly for male sexual problems. E.J. Banfield, famous as a beachcomber in Far North Queensland, recommends the tuber as a vegetable, having a 'crisp and slightly bitter' taste. It is advisable not to eat native plants unless you are quite sure of their identity and edibility, as many are poisonous. There is some interest in the export potential of plants such as Brahmin Ginseng, added to a list of emerging indigenous crops that might have future potential. The plants are inclined to grow on well drained hillside slopes, such as the Forgon Smith Spur, where this photograph was taken.

Ht 300-400mm Lf 300-400mm Fl Jan?

180 Yellow Button

Helichrysum rupicola is a flowering herb, growing up to 2 metres in height, and bearing small (10-20mm) papery flowers, which can be white, yellow or orange (Right). 'Rupicola' means living on rocks, and these plants are often to be found in rocky habitats within open forest, as well as in disturbed rainforest. Australians call a variety of papery flowers that retain their form and colour for long periods 'everlasting daisies'. Yellow buttons are not daisies, but they might fit the bill otherwise. These were growing at Mt. Whitfield.

181 Dianella

Four species of *Dianella* are found in North Queensland bordering rainforest areas, all with blue or purple flowers and berries. The leaves are often grasslike, but the flower stalk is usually 1 to 2 metres high (Right), with flowers and fruit appearing throughout the year. Some people call these 'Ground Orchids', but Dianella belongs to the Lily family, like the related Fringed Violet (no 426). The flowers often emerge from the grassy understorey in open forest. The plants vary. Some, like the one at left, grow long grass-like leaves from the butt of the plant, while in others (Above) the leaves radiate from the top of a short stem. Sometimes the leaves have a pink colour. The leaves produce a strong silky fibre that Aboriginal people used for weaving cord or baskets. The fruit and roots of some species are edible, and the fruit is a source of blue dye.

182 Arrowroot

Tacca leontopetaloides is a herb, rather lily-like as it emerges from its underground tuber, but it lacks the striking flowers of lilies. The flower spike and curled leaves arise at the same time on separate stems, and are mottled brown to green in colour (Right). The flower is quite unusual, like an avant garde flower arrangement, with ribbon like bracts and leaflike structures on the top of a ribbed stem that can be almost 2 metres tall (Left). The arrowroot used in thickening foods comes from the tubers, up to 10cm across, which can be up to 25% starch. The crushed tubers are washed several times to remove bitterness, and produce a rich, easily digested natural starch. Although most commercial arrowroot now comes from other plants, arrowroot is still produced in places like the Marshall Islands, where imported starch foods are expensive.

183 Oak Leaf Fern

Drynaria quercifolia is an attractive large fern found on rocks in open forest, or on river margins and rainforest edges. The fertile fronds can be up to 1 metre in length, and correspondingly broad, with the sori containing the spores in rows on each side of the secondary veins. However the name derives from the shape of the much smaller nest leaves, at the base of the large fronds, which trap mulch and nutrients. These mimic the shape of English Oak leaves ('quercifolia' means 'oak leaved'). (See no 83 for a close relative, often given the same common name.)

Oak Leaf Fern is found across tropical Australia, from the Cape York Peninsula in Qld through the NT to WA. It makes a good garden fern, but is frost tender.

184 Pigeon Grass

Setaria surgens is an attractive short grass with fluffy, bottle brush shaped seed heads, growing in open forest at the foot of Mt Cook near Cooktown.

It is a native of SE Asia and northern Australia, occurring in WA, the NT, and in north Queensland. It can reach 900mm in height, though the grass in the photograph was only half that height. The seeds are eaten by Black Throated Finches and Squatter Pigeons. It is also known as Annual Pigeon Grass, or Annual Setaria.

Other Plants from Coastal Open Forest

The plants that follow are a partial listing of species included elsewhere in this book that are also to be found in Coastal Open Forest.

TREES: Mueller's Damson *(Terminalia muelleri)* #33 p24
Lancewood *(Acacia crassicarpa)* #35 p24 **Umbrella Tree** *(Schefflera actinophylla)* #41 p27
Broad Leaved Paperbark *(Melaleuca viridiflora)* #44 p28 **Bushman's Clothes Pegs** *(Grevillea glauca)* #379 p171
Turpentine *(Syncarpia glomulifera)* #389 p152 **Cooktown Ironwood** *(Erythrophleum chlorostachys)* #401 p156
Weeping Bottlebrush *(Callistemon viminalis)* #436 p168 **African Tulip** *(Spathodea campanulata)* #437 p169
Creek Lilly Pilly *(Syzygium australe)* #439 p169 **River Cherry** *(Syzygium tierneyanum)* #441 p170
River Oak *(Casuarina cunninghamiana)* #443 p171

VINES: Derris *(Derris sp* (Daintree)*)* #414 p161 **Gidee Gidee** *(Abrus precatorius)* #417 p162
Rock Rosemary *(Merremia quinquefolia)* #419 p162

FERNS: Common Bracken *(Pteridium esculentum)* #420 p163

HERBS: Scarlet-flowered Blood-root *(Haemodorum coccineum)* #427 p165 **Sensitive Weed** *(Mimosa pudica)* #460 p176
Dark Blue Snakeweed *(Stachytarpheta cayennensis)* #457 p175 **Cusara Pea** *(Crotalaria zanzibarica)* #464 p178

OTHER: Northen Forest Grass Tree *(Xanthorrhoea johnsonii)* #423 p164

THE RAINFOREST

While many tourists come to Far North Queensland just to see the tropical rainforest, really getting to know it is not easy. For a start, this is such a complex ecosystem that no single person could ever claim to know it all. Even to become familiar with just the plant life in the rainforest is possibly more than one person could achieve in a lifetime. The main tropical rainforest plant guide lists over 2000 plants, and this covers just trees, shrubs and vines. Herbs, mosses, ferns and orchids are barely touched upon. New species continue to be found.

To add to the complexity, the rainforest is not everywhere the same. Rainforest ecologists have developed many categories that take account of the variation in rainforest throughout the wet tropics. High altitude rainforest differs from coastal rainforest, and is different again to the drier Mabi forest found on the deep basaltic soils of the Atherton Tablelands. In some areas very ancient plants are preserved in refugia, mostly on high mountains, where rainforest has persisted in drier periods in the past. Pollen deposited in lakes shows that many areas covered by rainforest today were once home to drier open forest.

For walkers, the sheer scale of the forest makes taking it in difficult. Walking through mature rainforest one is struck by the boles of trees, especially the strangler figs and those with buttress roots, the vines, and perhaps some of the smaller understory plants. If you stand and watch a while, you will be more aware of epiphytes on the limbs high above, but rarely do you see the canopy with any clarity. Canopy walks and Skyrail have made it easier to view this part of the forest, but these cover very limited areas.

As this book has been produced to assist with identification of plants as they are encountered by visitors or residents walking in the rainforest, inevitably the focus is on rainforest edges and the understory plants within the rainforest. Walkers will come across fallen fruit, but to illustrate even these is a huge project. A beautiful new book, 'Fruits of the Australian Tropical Rainforest', by Wendy and William T. Cooper, illustrates over 1200 of these in 600 large pages. Remember that many fruits are poisonous to us, even if eaten by birds or animals.

So from this rich diversity the following pages include a sampling of plants. Some of the rainforest species that cross the boundary into the neighbouring open forest have already been described. The photograph (Left) was taken on the Kuranda Range, and shows a **Flame Tree** (*Brachychiton acerifolius*) in bloom , above a **tree fern** (*Cyathea cooperi*) and rainforest trees.

185 Queensland Kauri (Kauri Pine) (Primitive)

Agathis robusta is one of three Agathis species found in North Queensland. All three belong to the Araucariaceae family linked to Gondwana, the ancient super continent that later broke into Australia, South America, etc. The leaves are not needles, though they have parallel veins. The fruit is a large cone the size of two fists (Below) made up of about 400 scales which surround the thin winged seeds.

Kauri pines are the largest trees in Queensland with diameters to 3 metres. Queensland Kauri has a smooth, often pinkish trunk, the bark shedding as scales. The timber is a valuable softwood, much sought after for ply-wood and furniture making. Most of the big trees were felled a century ago, but some impressive specimens still remain on Smith's Track near Cairns.

Ht >50m Lf 50-130mm Cones Nov-Feb 90-150mm

186 Bull Kauri (Primitive Plant)

Agathis microstachya is best known from the two giant Kauri trees at Lake Barrine (Left). These trees, at 45m, are close to the 50m maximum height for this species, and with a girth of 6m, they are the largest conifers in Australia. The brownish bark is shed as coarse scales. The leaves have parallel veins, and the fruits resemble those of the Kauri above. Separate male and female cones are produced.

Bull Kauri are found only on the Atherton Tableland between 600-1000m above sea level. The Araucariaceae, the family to which Kauri and Bunya pines belong, dominated vegetation during the Mesozoic era (250-65m years ago) along with the Cycads. The modern members of these families are similar to the fossilized remains of their ancestors and are in a sense living fossils, giving us an insight into the ancestors of most modern plants. It is remarkable that these plants survived climate change and the volcanic activity that shaped the Atherton Tablelands where they now exist. In all 13 species of conifer occur in the Wet Tropics, 5 nowhere else.

Ht >50m   Lf 20-90mm   MaleCones Nov 11-30mm   Female Cones Dec-Jan 75-120mm

187 Bunya Pine (Primitive Plant)

Araucaria bidwillii is another large conifer found in two small areas in North Queensland (Mt Lewis and the Cannabullen Falls near Ravenshoe) and also in a larger area on the Bunya Mts in Southern Queensland. Most of the trees spread across the Atherton Tableland, like the one pictured, have been planted since white settlement. Bunya pines form an attractive conical form suited to large gardens. Hoop Pine belongs to the same family and is also found in Far North Queensland. A jurassic age fossil (*A. mirabilis*) is closely related to the Bunya Pine. Bunya pines grow stiff spiny leaves. The male cones are borne in Nov, while the later female cones contain 50-100 seeds up to 50mm long. Fruiting usually occurs every three years. As a full grown cone can weigh 10kg they can be dangerous when falling. Aboriginal people ate the nuts and would gather for large intertribal feasts at the Bunya Mountains during this period of food surplus. Logging was banned by Gov. Gipps in 1842, but from 1860 it was re-allowed and many trees were felled. Queenslands second national park was declared in 1908 to protect the remainder.

Ht >50m   Lf 10-50mm   Male Cones Nov >200mm   Female Cones Dec-Feb >300mm

188 Brown Pine (Primitive Plant)

Podocarpus grayae is a tree with dark pencil shaped leaves that are a bright lime green when new. The leaves hang attractively from the the thin, somewhat drooping branches (Right). The tree carries leaves with inturned edges, a dominant mid vein, and indistinct parallel veins. Although closely related to pine trees it does not grow a cone but a bluish hard nut is carried on the end of a swollen red stem, that looks like a fruit and which is eaten by birds such as the Cassowary. The trunk is straight and the bark is fissured and a little inclined to peel. The timber is useful but comparatively rare and has been used for piano keys and violin bellies, amongst other things. This tree is quite common around Kuranda. The shiny pencil shaped leaves make it easy to identify. The family to which Brown Pine belongs has an ancient lineage, having changed little from the days of the dinosaurs. Today this species, also known as **Northern Brown Pine**, one of four rainforest Podocarpus species, is found from near Cape York to near Townsville.

Ht >30m   Lf 85-250mm   Male Cones Apr-Jul 20-60mm   Fr Oct-Jan 10-20mm

189 Black Pine (Primitive Plant)

Sundacarpus amara is closely related to the Brown Pine (Above) but has now been given its own genus, of which it is the single species. This tree may be buttressed (unusual for this family) but the trunk is not distinctive, unlike the Brown Pine, so it is the dark foliage that usually attracts attention. The leaves resemble those of the Brown Pine but have undulating margins. Male cones occur in small bunches and the fruit are almost spherical, red or orange, with a large seed. Black Pine occurs in a small area of Far North Queensland, between Kuranda and Townsville, also in India, SE Asia and in PNG, where it can reach 60m and is a valuable timber tree. The leaves taste sweet when chewed but quickly turn bitter (the meaning of *amara*). The scientific name has been picked up in internet dictionaries and used to create internet junk.

Ht >40 Lf 50-170mm M. Cones Jul-Aug 25-40mm Fr Dec-Feb 25-35mm

190 Rose Gum

Eucalyptus grandis is one of the superb Eucalypt species in Australia. These big trees grow on ridges in rainforest (above 600m) or on the edge of rainforest. The large growth (Right) is a burl caused by insect attack. The wood in burls is often highly figured and used for decorative effect. Unfortunately the timber of this species is often marked by Scribbley Borers and grubs, reducing its value. The long straight trunks (Left) are unsuitable for power poles as they do not take preservative well. Overseas Rose Gum is widely planted for woodchip, paper and timber production. Rose gum, or **Flooded Gum**, is also known as 'the widow maker' as it can drop branches without warning. These trees grow from Mt Spurgeon near Cairns to Newcastle, NSW.

Ht >70m Lf 80-170mm Fl Apr-Aug Fr any month 5-8mm

191 Black Wattle (Brown Salwood)

Acacia celsa is one of the pioneer species in rainforest, growing rapidly whenever damage to the canopy allows light to penetrate. The soft, even canopy of blueish foliage is very common around Kuranda where this and related species are the dominant vegetation in areas long ago cleared for farming and then abandoned. At first it can form a monoculture; other species take root below it and eventually replace it. In perhaps eighty years it dies. Large Black Wattle trees in the rainforest are signs of earlier disturbance, usually from a cyclone or logging. The timber is hard with an attractive grain, used for furniture, though it reacts with metals. This

is one of several wattles known as 'Black Wattle'; Brown Salwood was the foresters' name for this species. The creamy-yellow flowers open for a few days only. The curled pods (40-130mm) are diagonally ribbed, containing several black seeds.

Ht >30m   Lf 50-155mm   Fl Jan-May   Fr Oct-Jan

192 Tasmanian Blackwood

Acacia melanoxylon is a wattle that grows from Tasmania to Far North Queensland, producing an atractive dark cabinet timber. It grows at higher altitudes as far north as Mt Spurgeon, inland from Mossman, and is common near Ravenshoe. The tree bears straight to sickle shaped leaves (actually phyllodes, or flattened leaf stalks). Young trees (above Left) have juvenile compound leaves attached to the ends of the phyllodes. The pale yellow flowers are followed by brown, coiled, sometimes sticky pods. Aboriginal people used the hard wood for tools and weapons and the bark for string and a medication for sore joints. The tree has been exported for timber production and is now a weed in South Africa. The sawdust can cause asthma.

Ht >20m(Nth Qld)   Lf 40-160mm   Fl Nov-May   Fr Sep-Nov&Apr 30-150mm

193 Red Cedar

Toona ciliata is perhaps Australia's most valuable tree species, once known as 'Red Gold' due to the value of its soft, light, but very beautiful cabinet timber. Cedar getters were often the first white men to explore the 'scrubs' of the coastal ranges, searching for this tree, which grows to a huge girth. The largest tree left blew down in 2006 near Lake Eacham on the Atherton Tablelands. Red Cedar has been difficult to grow as a plantation timber as it is attacked by the Cedar Tip Moth that damages the growing tip, spoiling the trunk. The compound leaves (Top, Left) resemble many other rainforest species, but the rather flaking bark is more distinctive, similar to the related Cedar Mangrove (See no 9). The flowers are white or cream in open sprays (Above, Left). The fruits (Left) ripen to a brown, woody 5 valved capsule, containing about 25 seeds. Red Cedar trees can be seen beside the road in the Tolga Scrub between Tolga and Atherton. A section of a cedar log, from the old logging days, is on display in a corner arcade of shops in Kuranda.

Ht >45m   Lf 40-150mm   Fl Sep-Nov 6-12mm   Fr Sep-Jan&May 10-22mm

194 Briar Oak (White Oak) (Primitive Plant)

Musgravea heterophylla, like many rainforest trees, has very different juvenile and adult leaves. The name 'heterophylla' means 'different leaved'. The leaves shown (Right) are the lobed juvenile form, athough this was already quite a large tree, growing beside the suspended walkway at the Barron Falls near Kuranda close to the top lookout. The rusty velvety hairs that cover the growing tips of the branches are similar to those which cover the flower stalks and the fruit capsules (held upwards at the ends of the branches) which split open to release a thin winged seed. These juvenile leaves are very large and striking whereas the adult leaves are unremarkable. Fossils of a similar tree have been found in Victoria dating from the Eocene period. Related to the Banksias, there are only two species of Musgravea, both occurring only in Australia. Briar Oak is found in the restricted area between Cooktown and Mission Beach. The reddish mottled timber is good for turning.

Ht >30m   Lf 50-220mm   Fl Mar-Apr   Fr Nov-Jan 70-95mm

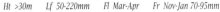

195 Northern Silky Oak (Bull Oak) (Primitive Plant)

Cardwellia sublimis has long been an important source of good quality timber in Far North Queensland. The tree is most easily identified by the seed pods which jut out from the leaves against the sky. The compound leaves bear 6-20 leaflets arranged in pairs on short stalks with swollen bases. White or cream fragrant spikes of flowers are followed by large woody pods (80-150mm) (Left) bearing 6-12 winged seeds, eaten by Cockatoos and Bush Rats. Seedlings have characteristic 'butterfly wing' leaves (Left). Northern Silky Oak is the only species in its genus and it occurs only from Cooktown to Paluma in Far North Qld. The dark, oak-like timber once made up 15% of all timber production in the area.

Ht >35m Lf 70-210mm Fl Oct-Dec Fr Sep-Apr

196 Mueller's Silky Oak (Primitive)

Austromuellera trinervia is a rare and threatened species included here due to its being one of the famous primitive plants found at Cape Tribulation. It is increasingly used as an excellent ornamental tree of modest size and spectacular flowers. The leaves are compound, made up of from 12 to 32 strongly three-veined and unequal sided leaflets. These may be without leaf stalks. The fragrant flowers form outstanding cream or yellow spikes followed by very large upright seed pods each bearing 2 winged seeds. These trees can be seen from the Marrdja Boardwalk near Cape Tribulation (Left) if you have a knowledgable guide. They are found in a small area of North Queensland from Cooktown to the Atherton Tableland and are survivors of long periods in refugia when conditions were unfavourable. They are regarded as 'living fossils'.

Ht >18m   Lf 75-190mm   Fl Nov-Jan   Fr Jul-Nov 140-210mm

197 Golden Oak

Grevillea baileyana is named after a famous Queensland botanist, F. M. Bailey, responsible for much of the early work on the flora of the state. This tree is a beautiful memorial to him. Golden Oak is a Grevillea, a family of plants almost confined to Australia, where there are 357 species. Only four of these grow in and around rainforest and one of these is introduced from further South (See no 478). The flowers of the Golden Oak can be quite prolific in green, white or cream masses. The seedlings (Below, Right) have deeply divided leaves. Adult leaves, particularly the new growth, can be truly spectacular. The underside of the leaves (Left) can vary from silver to gold, with the new growth on the tips of the branches having the most intense gold colour. To watch the branches blown by the wind while lit by yellow afternoon light is one of the great pleasures of living in the wet tropics.

Ht >30m   Lf 60-300mm   Fl Aug-Dec
Fr Oct-Feb 12-19mm

198 Zamia Palm
(Primitive Plant)

Lepidozamia hopei is the only species from this ancient family still found in the rainforest. It is probably the world's tallest cycad. The male cone is shown (Right), while the larger female cone produces about 100 red fruits (Below). These fruits are toxic and may take up to a year to germinate. Zamia Palms can be found on Mt. Whitfield near the Cairns Botanic Gardens.

The Zamia Palm, also called **Hope's Cycad**, is what remains of a vegetation that flourished 240 million years ago. Pollination was believed to be by wind, but is more probably aided by beetles and weevils, possibly attracted to these plants by heat or odors. The Palm Cycad (no 139) resembles the Zamia Palm but usually grows in open forest with fronds less than 2m in length.

Ht >18m Lf 2-3m leaflets 200-400mm Male cones 250-700mm Female cones May-Jun 400-800mm

199 Black Bean

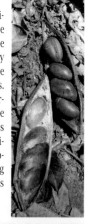

Castanospermum australe is a rainforest tree with a beautiful dark wood that was used for cabinetmaking, now scarce and expensive. In some trees the great contrast between the pale yellow sapwood and the almost black heartwood is very striking. Black Bean can be seen in Kuranda and Cairns, where it is used as a street tree, and it is common on river banks. The yellow/orange flowers (Left) are attractive, but are carried on the major branches so are somewhat hidden by the shiny compound leaves. BlackBean is pollinated by flying foxes and birds. The seed pods are large and borne in large quantities (Left) with 1-5 big seeds in each (Right). Aboriginal people ate the seeds, which are poisonous, after slicing, leaching and baking them to remove the saponins. The tree produces alkaloids with anti-HIV and anti-cancer properties.

Ht >35m   Lf 50-200mm Fl Jul-Jan 30-40mm Fr Mar-Nov 90-250mm

200 Bumpy Satinash

Syzygium cormiflorum is a cauliflorous tree, meaning the fruit are usually borne on the trunk. The flowers are fluffy and stamenous, green, white, cream or pink in colour and they can occur throughout the year. The fruits of some trees (Right) grow on the larger branches (known as ramiflory). The fruit can be as large as an apple, and contain a large seed surrounded by soft pithy flesh, eaten by Cassowaries. Bumpy Satinash has a dense canopy of dark leaves, with pink or purple new growth. It is most likely to be noticed when carrying flowers, or fruiting, though the knobs on the trunk from which the flowers and fruits emerge are distinctive at any time.

Bumpy Satinash is native to the area betwen Iron Range in Cape York and Ingham. 47 species of Syzygium are found in the rainforest, many growing along streams where they produce small brightly coloured fruits. They are often known as Lilly Pillies.

Ht >30m   Lf 60-210mm   Fl any month 8-15mm   Fr Sep-Jun 30-70mm

201 Northern White Beech

Gmelina fasciculiflora bears the most striking purple fruit, which when crushed smell of bleach and stain the fingers brown. The fruit from some trees is greatly deformed, presumedly from insect attack, while others, like those pictured, are intact. The tree bears fruit between Aug and May. The leaves are whitish underneath with a few flat glands near the base. This small tree (Left) is on the walking track on Mt. Whitfield. The timber is firm and close grained, the colour pale straw to a light grey brown, and is used for carving, boat building and pattern making, being very stable. It is considered the best carving wood in Queensland though a bit drab. It is also very slow to rot in the rainforest, eroding into distinctive pits on the surface of the wood.

Northern White Beech is found only from Cardwell to Cape Tribulation and is one of four species of Gmelina in Australia.

Ht >30m   Lf 50-160mm   Fl Sep-Jan 10-18mm   Fr Aug-May 10-30mm

202 Quandong

Elaeocarpus sp (Mossman Bluff) is a shrub or small tree with fragrant bell-shaped flowers and leaf stalks which are red and swollen at each end. Like its close relative the Blue Quandong (no 40), it has radiating leaves with an occasional colourful red or orange leaf amongst the green. The tree is small and coppices readily. The shiny leaves may be toothed or have smooth edges. The photo (Left) was taken at the top of Kahlpahlim Rock in the Lamb Range near Cairns, where this small tree was blooming at the base of a huge granite rock. The reddish stalks and attractive flowers, followed by blue or black berries, on a smallish tree, make this a species suitable for gardens. This is a little known species and the flower is listed as unknown in one of the main botanical resources, so flowering is perhaps rare.

This Quandong grows only between Thornton Peak and Lamb Range.

Ht >15m   Lf 50-100mm   Fl Nov-Dec   Fr May-Jun 15-17mm

203 Eumundi Quandong

Elaeocarpus eumundi is a rainforest tree, distinguishable as a Quandong by the occasional orange-red leaf, and bearing large crops of greenish blue marble sized fruits. This tree could be seen at the carpark at Lake Eacham before Cyclone Larry. Eumundi Quandong trees may be buttressed. The leaves are simple but can be somewhat toothed towards the end and are carried on long leaf stalks (10-55mm). The fragrant white or cream finely fringed flowers are followed by the fruit. These are eaten by fruit doves, Cassowaries, Figbirds, Spotted Catbirds, Spectacled Flying Foxes and Bush Rats. Eumundi Quandong occurs between Coen in Cape York and northern NSW. As an ornamental tree which tolerates cold and produces attractive reddish new growth, it is said to be "the trendiest large tree in Australia at present".

Ht >30m   Lf 40-200mm   Fl Nov-Dec 20-26mm   Fr Mar-Jan 14-20mm

204 Mountain Quandong

Elaeocarpus elliffii was named after a messenger at the Royal Botanical Gardens at Kew. It tends to be found in higher rainforest, as the name suggests, but does occur at lower levels too. The metallic blue or green fruits are typical of many Quandongs, of which 24 species occur in the wet tropics rainforest. The fruit follow white or cream 5-petalled fragrant flowers. There are distinctive marks on each side of the mid rib of the leaves where the main veins join. These are known as foveoles, and are like pockets, often containing hairs, large enough to become a home for mites. On these leaves they are clearly visible from the top surface of the leaf, though they are on the underside. There are about 9-18 teeth on each side of the leaf. Mountain Quandong occurs from Cooktown to Paluma. Cockatoos attack the branches and break them off.

Ht >36m   Lf 60-90mm   Fl Nov-Dec 10mm   Fr May-Oct 12-14mm

205 Hard Milkwood

Alstonia muelleriana is one of the pioneer species in disturbed rainforest, growing rapidly from a seedling (Right) with soft hairy leaves to a tree of 25 metres. The leaves are commonly in whorls of three or four. The masses of white flowers are followed by long paired green pods turning to brown (Left). The milky sap is white and sticky. Although found in a rather small area of North Queensland (Shipton's Flat to Paluma) and in PNG, Hard Milkwood has long been known as a source of alkaloids, and a book has been written about the alkaloids derived from this one plant. This is a tree which is energised by fire. Burning causes it to sucker from the roots, increasing the number of plants in the burnt area. This is a common tree in regenerating rainforest.

*Ht >25m   Lf 50-190mm   Fl Sep-Mar 5mm
Fr Aug-May 120-470mm*

206 Milky Pine

Alstonia scholaris is another pioneer species, similar to the related Hard Milkwood (Above) in the flowers and fruits it bears. However the leaves are larger, in whorls of 4 to 8, and are glossy on top and somewhat whitish underneath. The tree is straight and the wood is light in colour, and in density, leading to its use in net floats in Borneo, as a light wood for coffins in Sri Lanka, and as sanded planks used as 'slates' for school children to write on. It occurs in Australia from Cape York to Sarina, but extends through SE Asia to India and China. The tree in the photograph is growing on Mt Whitfield in Cairns. Milky Pine, or **White Cheesewood**, has been used as a medicine chest by many cultures, treating such diverse problems as malaria, toothache, rheumatism and snake bite. By the late 19th century three alkaloids had been identified from the bark. Homoeopaths use it to treat dysentery. Research continues into the compounds isolated from this tree.

Ht >40m   Lf 115-230mm   Fl Sep-Jan 5-12mm   Fr Jan-Apr 150-450mm

207 Damson (Sovereignwood) (Butterfly Plant)

Terminalia sericocarpa stands out briefly from the rainforest background after it winters (Sep-Oct). The lime green new growth (Right) can be seen in Nov across the face of the Kuranda Range. Later the Damson trees may be discriminated by the smallish leaves, the somewhat layered appearance of the branches (Left), and their upward sweep. The fruit is a small pink to purple-black drupe covered in fine hairs. The name 'sericocarpa' means 'fruits clothed in silky hairs'. The pointed seed is woody and hard. The timber is pale brown, easy to dry and work, and is suitable for joinery, but not for exposed situations. The grain is sometimes interlocked. Provided green ants are present, it will host colonies of three kinds of Oak-blue butterflies. Eclectus Parrots enjoy the fruits. Aboriginal people ate the fruit, which can be made into jams and wine. (Never risk eating rainforest fruits of which you are not absolutely sure.)

Ht >40m Lf 60-135mm Fl Sep-Dec 6-8mm Fr Nov-May 13-18mm

208 Native Hydrangea

Abrophyllum ornans grows as a rather untidy shrub or small tree in rainforest. The leaves are large and striking with deep parallel veins at about 40 degrees to the mid vein, and with a few hairs on the upper surface. The green, white or cream flowers are fragrant, and are followed by small black or purple berries, at any time of year. The tree (Right) grows over the path at Crystal Cascades.

Native Hydrangea, one of two Abrophyllum species, found only in Australia, occurs from Coen to NSW.

Ht >8m Lf 45-220mm Fl Oct-Jan Fr 8-12mm

209 Bleeding Heart (Butterfly Plant)

Homalanthus novoguineensis is conspicuous due to the occasional bright orange or red heart-shaped leaf amongst the glossy green foliage (Left). Because of its rapid growth it is often used for revegetation where rainforest is being re-established. Young trees can form a very regular umbrella shape and the long leaf stalks are often bright red. The stems are soft and exude a white sap when broken. The tree will eventually grow to 25 metres when it may be buttressed. The fruits are small green to purple capsules containing two brown seeds, attractive to many species of birds, including Birds of Paradise, Bower Birds and Pigeons. Ringtail Possums eat the leaves. The beautiful dark wood was used for cabinetmaking. This is also the host tree for the Hercules Moth, the world's largest moth with a wingspan of about 300mm, which is found in North Queensland. The caterpillar (>120mm) grows to the size of a man's thumb and can emit a loud rattle, likely to startle any predator. The Bleeding Heart is found North of Townsville in Qld, also in the NT and WA, and into SE Asia.

Ht >25m   Lf 40-230x25-230mm   Fl any month   Fr Nov-Feb 8-10mm

210 Pink Ash (Butterfly Plant)

Alphitonia petriei is closely related to Red Ash (no 42), which also grows in and around rainforest. It is a pioneer species, the saplings (Left) growing rapidly in disturbed areas. The leaves can be fairly large, dull green on top, whitish below, and often with a layered effect. Masses of white, cream or green flowers cover the branches and are pollinated by beetles. The fruit (Right) ripen to black, the outer shell falling

away to leave three orange to red seeds still attached to the plant, surrounded by powdery flesh. Many birds feast on these. The tree, found from Cape York to northern NSW, is a host to the Small Green Banded Blue butterfly. Pink Ash is one of many rainforest trees that contain bioactive chemicals. Research at Paluma found more than half the trees tested showed marked bioactivity, meaning they could produce valuable drugs. This tree contains methyl salicylate, responsible for the linament-like smell, hence the common name **Sarsaparilla**.

Ht >40m   Lf 65-180mm   Fl Sep-Mar 5mm   Fr Jan-Jul 7-8mm

211 Native Mangosteen

Garcinia warrenii is quite common in rainforest around Kuranda, where the thick leathery leaves, often stained with growths of mould or perhaps lichen, are the chief distinguishing feature. If a leaf is broken, a sticky, ochre yellow exudate soon emerges. The leaf tends to snap readily when creased. Trees that grow straight up into the canopy will generally not have low branches, and are therefore unlikely to be noticed. But trees such as the one shown have drooping branches and the rather large, untidily placed leaves may stand out. The fruit is about the size of a fig, smooth, and yellow, red, purple or blackish in colour. The fruit may cover the ground under the trees. The Cairns Botanic Gardens describes the Native Mangosteen as "a bushy tree with highly fragrant, white flowers and sweet edible purple fruit." The true Mangosteen (*Garcinia mangostana*) is thought by many to be the queen of all tropical fruit but no-one is claiming this for the Native Mangosteen. It is a tree which shows monoecy, with both male and female flowers on one tree, possibly at different times, to attract sluggish pollinators such as thrips or beetles.

Ht >15m Lf 70-180mm Fl Jul-Sep >18mm Fr Oct-Feb 40-58mm

212 Native Nutmeg

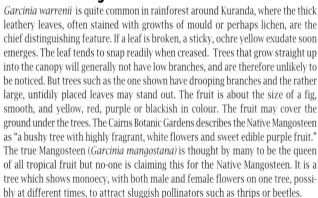

Myristica insipida (and the closely related *Myristica globosa*) are related to the true Nutmeg. As the name 'insipida' suggests, this fruit has been tried as a substitute for Nutmeg with mediocre results. The trees are common adjacent to the Cairns Botanic Gardens on Mt. Whitfield, and have a light and open radiating branch structure that makes them stand out. The leaves also are somewhat whitish underneath and are carried daintily on the thin branches. The brown pods split open to reveal a darker brown seed almost surrounded by a red covering. *M. insipida* is hairier and has more rounded leaves than *M. globosa*. These trees practice 'pollination by deceit', with male trees luring beetles which also visit the synchonised flowering females in the area. The fruits are the favourite food of the Pied Imperial Pigeon, and also attract Cassowaries, Rifle-birds, and Musky Rat Kangaroos. They are found in SE Asia and in Far North Qld south to Mission Beach.

Ht >25m   Lf 90-245mm   Fl Nov-Jun 8-12mm   Fr Jan-Feb 25-40mm

213 Grey Bollywood (Butterfly Plant)

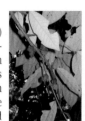

Neolitsea dealbata is a widely distributed small tree with distinctive foliage. The leaves are typically white underneath. Often the white coating has been rubbed off as leaves brush against each other in the wind. Young trees resemble the open upwardly branching form of Native Nutmeg (Above) but the leaves are commonly borne in groups of three. Young leaves may be coppery and hang limply. The fruits are small (about 10mm across) and turn red or black when ripe (Right). They

are eaten by many species of bird, including the Brown Cuckoo Dove, Topknot and White-headed Pigeons, and the Green Catbird. Flying Foxes are also attracted to the fruit and several species of butterfly use this plant, also called **White Bollygum**.

Grey Bollywood occurs from Wollongong in NSW to Cape York, and in PNG. The effectiveness of pollination depends on the proximity of the male and female plants.

Ht >15m   Lf 80-220mm   Fl Mar-Jul 4-12mm   Fr Jan-Jul 8-11mm

Rainforest - Trees

214 Black Walnut (Queensland Walnut)

Endiandra palmerstonii is one of Australia's great cabinet timbers, with a heartwood of grey-brown, streaked with chocolate, black and pink. The wavy grain produces figured wood, making this a popular veneer. As the wood contains silica, it is difficult to cut. The tree is often buttressed and can exude a smelly black substance. The cut wood also has an unpleasant odour. The leaves are simple and pale on the underside, which is clothed in white or pale brown hairs. Tiny white to yellow fragrant flowers are followed by large ribbed fruits. These are yellow, orange or brown spheres, and are eaten by feral pigs and Giant White-tailed Rats. The large seeds are toxic to humans but the Ngadjonji Aboriginal people of the Malanda area crushed the nuts with special stone grinders, allowing the fruit to be cooked and eaten. Black Walnut occurs in only a small area from Kuranda to Cardwell. It is one of over thirty species of Endiandra in North Queensland. Wonderful specimens can be seen at Malanda opposite the falls.

Ht >40m   Lf 70-225mm   Fl Nov-Mar   Fr Sep-Apr 45-60mm

215 Sankey's Walnut

Endiandra sankeyana is another Walnut of the Northern rainforest. The tree bears simple leaves with whitish hairs underneath and a depressed midrib on top. Small flowers are followed by blue-black or black elongated fruit which smell of cologne when cut. The fruits are eaten by Cassowaries, Musky Rat-kangaroos, and Bush Rats. Sankey's Walnut occurs from Cedar Bay to Ingham.

Ht > 30m   Lf 80-170mm   Fl Oct-Dec   Fr May-Nov 25-58mm

216 Brown Currajong

Commersonia bartramia is a small tree that grows masses of white or cream fragrant flowers so dense that they resemble snow on the layered branches. Flowering at Christmas, it is also known as **Scrub Christmas Tree**. The fragrant flowers are followed by brown, bristly fruit (left of Photo Below). The top of the leaves can be sandpapery, while the underside is thickly covered with white hairs. This small tree can be separated from the similar Red Ash (no 42) and Pink Ash (no 210) by the serrated leaf edge and the bristly 5 valved fruit. The inner bark produces a strong fibre used by Aboriginal people for nets, while the wood burns well. In Fiji the tree has medicinal uses. Brown Currajong occurs from central NSW to Cape York and through PNG to SE Asia.

Ht > 25m   Lf 60-190mm   Fl Sep-Mar 5mm   Fr Jan-Aug 10-25mm (including bristles)

217 Red Tulip Oak

Argyrodendron peralatum is a large buttressed rainforest tree, one of nine Argyrodendron species found in North Queensland rainforests. The name means 'silver tree' and it is easily recognised once the shiny silver undersides of the leaves (Below) have been noticed. The leaves grow in groups of three, another aid to identification. The species name, 'peralatum', means 'completely winged', and refers to the brown spiky fruit, about 15mm in diameter, with a single 70mm long wing attached, which allows it to helicopter to the ground. Buttress roots like those

shown are not much help identifying trees as mature specimens of many species have buttresses. However the ridges in these roots are rather distinctive in Red Tulip Oaks. Red Tulip Oak is found between Cooktown and Tully. Some nice specimens can be seen at the Clohesy River Boardwalk.

Ht >35m Lf 70-75mm Fl Mar-Aug&Dec Fr Sep-Feb

218 Brown Tulip Oak

Argyrodendron polyandrum is a close relative of the Red Tulip Oak (Above) and has many similar features. The leaves are somewhat smaller but they grow in groups of three with a coppery or silvery underside. The fruits are also very similar, except the head is the size of a pea, and the single wing is only about 50mm long. The crowns of these trees have a bluish brown colouration in some lights that makes them stand out (Left).

Brown Tulip Oak is a very common species in rainforest with Kauri Pine, between Cape York and Gladstone, and the winged seeds are to be found on the rainforest floor from Oct to Jan. Like the Red Tulip Oak, it is often buttressed. Seeds from the tree illustrated have been seen to 'helicopter' for a distance of over 100 metres in a wind gust, which is testimony to the elegant simplicity of their design. When the seeds land on moisture they quickly exude a sticky gum which may anchor them until germination.

Ht >45m   Lf 50-120mm   Fl May-Oct 13-15mm   Fr Oct-Jan 60-70mm inc. wing

219 Hickory Ash

Flindersia ifflaiana is one of eleven species of Flindersia (named after pioneer navigator Matthew Flinders) found in the rainforest near Cairns. All grow five-valved woody capsules which separate as they ripen to release the thin winged seeds. The outside of these capsules is usually covered with bumps or short spines (Below). Hickory Ash is one of the more common species, growing into a large tree with rough bark and a usable timber. The leaves are compound. **Queensland Maple**, another Flindersia, is the source of a beautiful cabinet timber. It is when these trees are in flower that they stand out with dense heads of white or cream blossom covering the foliage like snow. It is common for all the trees in an area to

flower together, so the impact is visible across the landscape. There are a number of trees with similar flowers so identification may not be certain unless other features are checked.

Ht >35m Lf 50-135mm Fl Oct-Mar&Jun Fr Oct-Apr30-55mm

220 Silver Maple

Flindersia acuminata is a dense foliaged rainforest tree which grows large 5-valved fruits with a spiky exterior, that open to release about 20 thin winged seeds. The tree may be buttressed. From 3-15 shiny and unequal sided tapering leaflets make up each dark green compound leaf. Small white, cream, yellow or brown flower clusters precede the fruit. The thin brown seeds are held in layers within the valves and released when the valves open. This tree has been used in farm forestry plantings. Silver Maple is found only in a restricted area in the Wet Tropics, from the Windsor Tableland west of Mossman to Paluma north of Townsville. There are 17 species of Flindersia worldwide, 15 of which occur in Australia. They are named after Matthew Flinders, a famous navigator who charted much of the coast of Australia and who took with him on the *Investigator* the botanist Robert Brown. Silver Maple is valued for its now rare timber with a silvery sheen that explains its other common name of **Silver Silkwood**. It is used in cabinetmaking and for turning and carving.

Ht >40m   Lf 50-150mm   Fl Nov-Jan&May   Fr Jun-Mar 70-150mm

221 White Croton

Croton triacros is a shrub or small tree of rainforest margins with shiny, sometimes toothed, egg shaped leaves. The leaves on the tips of the branches are typically yellowish orange in colour, with a slight resemblance to the better known ornamental crotons of tropical gardens.

The tree grows tiny green, white or cream flowers followed by green 3 valved capsules (Right). This tree occurs from Iron Range to Mackay, and is one of a very large family of 1100 species worldwide, of which 18 are found in the rainforest of North Queensland.

The wood of this tree was used by Aboriginal people for spears, hence another common name of **Spear Birch**.

Ht >8m   Lf 50-185mm   Fl Oct-Jul   Fr Oct-Jul 5-8mm

222 Brown Laurel (Butterfly Plant)

Cryptocarya triplinervis is a medium sized rainforest tree often found on stream banks, with masses of fruit in season. The leaves are simple with a few dominant veins, often 3 veined, and with short leaf stalks. The tree will probably only be noticed when it is fruiting (Left) as it bears masses of black, olive like fruit, each bearing a single large brown stone. These fruits are eaten by Figbirds, Lewin's Honeyeaters, and King Parrots. It is also a host to two kinds of butterfly.

The Lauraceae family, to which the laurels belong, is one of the more difficult to identify by species. There are about 100 Laurels just in the North Queensland rainforest. This species occurs only from Iron Range to Ingham.

Ht 20m   Lf 45-135mm   Fl Aug-Oct   Fr Dec-Mar 8-13mm

FIGS

Fig trees, belonging to the *Ficus* family, are widespread in North Queensland, having adapted to a great variety of environments. They are most easily recognized by their fruit, which generally resemble the domestic fig in structure, where the flowers are actually produced within the 'fruits' (technically synconia). The form of the 30 local species varies greatly, ranging from some of the largest rainforest trees with multiple trunks or strangling habits, to small stunted trees growing on rocks in open forest. Stranglers start their life as an epiphyte high on another tree where a bird has deposited the seed. The small seedling will drop a fine threadlike root to the forest floor, followed by others which fuse together, strangling the host tree (Left). Banyans develop a forest of trunks, all interconnected, while other species drop roots from near the tips of the branches. Rock breaking figs grow in thin crevices in rock often levering the rock apart in the process. There is even a fig that grows as a vine. The famous Curtain Fig tree near Yungaburra is a modified strangler which fell against another tree, and the Cathedral Fig near Lake Tinaroo is a Banyan. There are some fine Banyan specimens on the Esplanade in Cairns and a great variety of species can be seen during a pleasant walk at Crystal Cascades.

223 Variegated Fig

Ficus variegata is a common fig at Cystal Cascades, where masses of fruit are borne on long stems, in bursts throughout the year, even on buttresses (Lower Right). Both green and red forms can be found there (Right & Below).

Variegated Figs grow to 30m, with large, shiny, almost heart shaped leaves on long stalks. Cassowaries, Double-eyed Fig Parrots and Flying Foxes eat the fruit. This tree is native to an area from Cape York to Paluma, and also occurs across the Pacific and in Asia. The timber has been used for boxes, etc, but not for construction. On Cape York peninsula these trees will drop their leaves during the dry season.

Ht >30m Lf 110-250mm Figs 20-30mm stalk 30-50mm

Rainforest - Figs

224 Weeping Fig

Ficus benjamina is a medium sized banyan (multiple trunked tree), with smallish smooth leaves that tend to hang downwards from descending branches. The fruits are small (Right) and shiny. They are pink, red, purple or black when ripe and are eaten by many birds and Spectacled Flying Foxes. The tree shown here stands on the Esplanade only metres from Cairns' busiest night spot and seems to thrive there. Weeping figs are generally found in low altitude rainforest near the coast.

Found in Queensland from Cape York to Mackay, this fig is also native to much of South Asia. The sap is poisonous, and can cause dermatitis and allergic reactions in some people. The huge size and aggresssive root system means it is not a good choice for a garden plant, but it is a favourite indoor and bonsai plant, though inclined to drop its leaves in response to changes in light or other stresses.

Ht >20m   Lf 30-120mm   Figs 8-12mm   stalks absent

225 Cluster Fig

Ficus racemosa grows figs in bunches on the trunk and larger limbs. They ripen to yellow, orange or red and attract many species of birds, flying foxes and feral pigs. Ripe fruit are about 35mm across on short stems similar to domestic figs. The leaves are moderately large and shiny (Left). The trees are deciduous. Though these are a rainforest fig, they are also found in drier forest and along river and creek banks, between Iron Range in Cape York and southern Queensland. They also grow in the NT, WA and SE Asia.

Traditional Indian medicine used the bark, fruits, roots and sap of this tree to treat many diseases. Recent scientific testing has confirmed the efficacy of its glycosides in lowering glucose in diabetes, assisting healing of wounds, and lowering high temperatures. It is also an anti-diuretic.

Ht >35m   Lf 50-200mm   Figs 30-35x35-40mm   stalks 5-12mm

226 Hairy Fig

Ficus hispida develops bunches of figs that hang on long stems from the trunk or larger branches of the tree. Fruit are borne throughout the year, ripening to green, cream or yellow. The fruit may be spotted and they are clothed in velvety white hairs, hence the common name. The rather untidy trees may develop a buttress but are relatively small. The leaves are opposed, sandpapery on top and softly hairy to sandpapery below. Fruit are eaten by Cassowaries, Double-eyed Fig Parrots and Figbirds. Hairy Fig occurs from Cape York to central Qld, and in the NT, WA, and SE Asia. Its alkaloids have been recently tested and shown to have strong anti diabetic, anti diarrhoeal, and anti cancer properties. Like all figs, the pollination is by specialised wasps that breed in the 'fruit' (known as synconia). Male trees of this species produce the wasps, which then pollinate the fruits of the female trees. Hairy Fig can look very different if the habitat differs. See no 383 for this same fig, showing a different form, growing in collapsed caves at Chillagoe.

Ht >13m   Lf 90-350mm   Figs any month 15-30x25-40mm   stalks 5-15mm

227 Watkin's Fig (Strangler Fig)

Ficus watkinsiana is a strangler fig that grows to 40 metres in height. Strangler figs enclose the host tree with aerial roots that grow down from a branch, but there is debate as to the cause of death of the host. It may just eventually die from old age. The leaves (Right) are large with a yellow midrib, shiny on top and shiny or hairy below. The fruit (Above) is distinctive, purplish with pale spots. It is edible and supposedly quite tasty. However, do not eat fruit you are not sure of as a mistake could be fatal. Watkin's Fig normally grows above 400 metres but is found at Kuranda. Many birds and Spectacled Flying Foxes feed on the fruit. Catbirds rely on the fruit of this tree as their principal item of diet and they carry fruit to the tops of other trees where they eat them. An Agonid wasp is also needed to pollinate the fruit. This fig grows between Cairns and Proserpine and also near the Qld/NSW border. It makes a good indoor plant.

Ht >40m   Lf 50-250mm   Figs Jul-Apr 20-40mm stalks 10-25mm

228 Red Leaf Fig

Ficus congesta is an unusual fig which grows its fruit on leafless stems or runners on the ground. The tree has a white or cream sap and produces large leaves which are hairy and sandpapery on both sides.

The figs grow, in pairs or clusters, on the branches and trunk, but it is the figs growing on what appears at first glance to be the roots that will attract attention. They are yellow and can be smooth or sandpapery. They are found at any time of year and are eaten by Double-eyed fig Parrots, Cassowaries or Spectacled Flying Foxes.

Red Leaf Fig is found from Cape York to Great Keppel Island, and in SE Asia and across the Pacific. It is used as a garden plant due to its large leaves which are bright red when new. It grows well in a tub. Aboriginal people ate the ripe fruits, and made string from the bark.

Ht >6m   Lf 90-250mm   Figs any month 15-28mm stalks 5-20mm

229 Rusty Fig

Ficus destruens is one of two figs commonly known as Rusty Figs. The fruits of this species are somewhat elongated with a pronounced protrusion on the end - the two species are otherwise difficult to separate. The tree, which is a strangler, has rusty hairy stems and leaf undersides. Leaves are smooth or hairy on top, rusty hairy underneath, and have longish stems. They tend to radiate around the branches. The figs are orange to dark red, often spotted, with fine rusty hairs, and are eaten by many bird species. Rusty Fig occurs from near Coen to Mackay. Aboriginal people ate the fruit raw or cooked and used the sticky sap to trap birds. The Rusty Fig is a useful shade tree and can live several hundred years. It sometimes grows as an epiphyte on eucalypts in open forest.

Ht >40m   Lf 50-194mm   Figs Sep-Jul 10-20mm stalks 3-6mm

230 Banana Fig

Ficus pleurocarpa is a fig with a distinctive elongated fruit that slightly resembles a banana. The tree is usually a strangler and has a white sap. The leaves are shiny with some hairs on the underside along the midrib. The leaf stalks are long and may be hairy. The stipules, at the tip of each branch, are up to 300mm long and may be yellow, orange or red. Ripe figs are orange or purple-red, usually spotted, and somewhat ribbed lengthwise. The stem of the fruit is long, thick, and flanged at the base. Many birds and animals eat the fruits. The Banana Fig occurs from near Cooktown to Tully. Aboriginal people ate the ripe fruit and hammered the inner bark to make blankets and containers to carry water or honey, or to leach bitter yams. Studies of microfungi have found more than 100 species in the decaying leaves of this one fig.

Ht >30m   Lf 120-280mm   Figs any month   35-65mm stalk 10-30mm

231 Septic Fig (Poisonous)

Ficus septica has a sap, which, if applied to raw flesh, will cause the surrounding flesh to rot. The tree produces a yellowish sap and bears large, shiny leaves with prominent veins and medium length leaf stalks. The stipules at the apex of each branch are green (12-50mm). The figs are found on the branches or trunk and are often carried on leafless stems. They are green to cream or brown, usually spotted and ribbed lengthwise, and are sandpapery to touch. The fruits are eaten by Spectacled Flying Foxes, Bush Rats and Double-eyed Fig Parrots.

Septic Fig occurs from Cape York to Mackay and in SE Asia, where at least 35 alkaloids and other chemicals have been found in the stems. Roots, fruits and leaves are used in traditional medicine. Many figs cause dermatitis, and this is one of them.

Ht >15m   Lf 80-250mm   Figs Jan&Jun 15-24mm stalks 20-50mm

232 White Fig

Ficus virens occurs in two varieties; one, with a short stem on the fruit, from Cape York to Gladstone; the second, without a stem, from Cape York to NSW. It is also found in the NT and WA and through PNG to Asia. The tree is a strangler or banyan and can be a dominant tree in the rainforest. It is deciduous, even in very wet areas, bearing simple shiny leaves on long stalks (20-70mm). The figs can be white with red spots, or pink, purple or black, and are eaten by many species of bird. Aboriginal people ate the fruits. The famous 'Curtain Fig' near Yungaburra, with a massive curtain of roots, is a White Fig, as is the equally impressive 'Cathedral Fig' near Lake Tinaroo. This latter is a banyan with many trunks. The fig (Left) in the Mossman Gorge, is a strangler with two major trunks and huge buttresses.

Ht >40m   Lf 40-190mm   Figs Sep-Jul 8-20mm

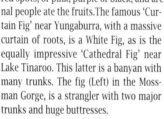

233 Fig

Ficus virgata is an open foliaged tree with long slender branches. The tree is often a strangler. The large shiny leaves have veins almost at right angles to the mid vein, with short stems, and often a flat gland on the underside near the base. The stipules at the ends of branches are small and pink. The figs are small and somewhat variable in shape, from spherical to elongated with a protrusion on the end. They are orange to red, or nearly black, on a short stalk, and are found throughout the year spread along the branches in large numbers. They are eaten by Metallic Starlings. This fig occurs from the Iron range to Paluma, and through PNG into Asia. In Pakistan the leaves were boiled in goat's milk and used to soften the arteries and the fruits used as a laxative. In India the shoots were eaten in famine.

Ht >30m   Lf 80-300mm   Figs any month 10-17mm   stalk 3-5mm

234 Candlenut

Aleurites rockinghamensis is a favoured timber for wood-chop competitions. It grows to a tall tree with a straight trunk which can have buttress roots. The seedlings slightly resemble the Bleeding Heart (no 209) but lack colour. The large shiny leaves in an open, untidy canopy are rather distinctive. During the wet season, some trees turn white with new leaves and flowers (Above, Left). The fruits will burn, and can be strung together to produce a primitive candle. Though poisonous, the fruit were cooked to reduce the toxins, then eaten by Aboriginal people. The fruits are bottled and sold in Asia. This tree occurs between Cooktown and Paluma, and in PNG. It is shortlived, with a lifespan of only 70-100 years.

Ht >40m   Lf 110-400   Fl Oct-Jun 10-12mm
Fr Mar-Dec 35-65mm

235 Northern Muttonwood (Butterfly Plant)

Rapanea porosa is an open-foliaged small tree which bears a prolific crop of purple berries on the stems. The tree has nicely layered almost horizontal branches with the leaves at the tips of the numerous side branches. The small white or cream flowers produce thousands of coffee-like purple, cream or black berries. The fruits are eaten by Figbirds, Metallic Starlings and Yellow Orioles. Northern Muttonwood occurs from Cape York to the Conondale ranges in SE Qld. It is the host for a Cape York 'Harlequin Metalmark' butterfly and a large yellow moth. It sells as an attractive container plant with red and maroon highlights in the foliage.

Ht >10m   Lf 40-180mm   Fl Jul-Nov   Fr Feb-Mar 4-6mm

236 Pink Euodia (Butterfly Plant)

Melifope elleryana is a common rainforest tree which is the host tree for the vivid blue Ulysses butterflies that abound in the Cairns and Kuranda area. It is also an attractive flowering tree, bearing masses of pink blossom on the stems. The tree may be buttressed, with the shiny leaves growing in groups of three, with longish leaf stalks. The pink (sometimes purplish or dark red) flowers are followed by clusters of greenish fruit, which are eaten by many birds. The flowers attract many butterflies.

The tree occurs from Cape York to northern NSW, also in the NT, WA, and through PNG to SE Asia. The sap was used as a glue or caulking compound in PNG. Zierone oil and evodione are produced from the leaves, and a flavenoid from the fruit.

Ht >35m Lf 45-260mm Fl Dec-Apr 10-14mm Fr Apr-Sep 5-13mm

237 Wheel-of-Fire

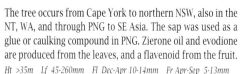

Stenocarpus sinuatus is a colourful flowering tree of the rainforest but the orange-red flowers are often missed as they cluster on the larger branches. Fallen flowers may be seen on the ground under the tree, though. The leaves may be simple, or lobed, or a mix of both, with sinuous edges. The lower photo shows the woolly grey fruit capsules (Centre) surrounded by a variety of the fallen leaves. The capsules contain packs of winged seeds. The flower (Left) has been scanned, and shows the wheel like arrangement of the parts. In cultivation, this is a slow tree to establish, and remains much smaller than in the rainforest. It normally grows on the ranges in North Qld.

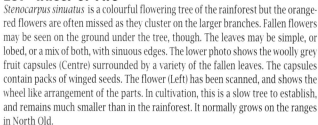

The Wheel-of-Fire tree is found in NE NSW and eastern Qld, and also in PNG. It has been widely grown as a street tree in countries as diverse as South Africa, the Scilly Isles, and the USA, where it is also used as an indoor plant. The timber is very attractive and suitable for cabinetwork, but is vulnerable to borers. It occurs naturally in the vicinity of Kuranda as well as being planted in gardens in the area.

Ht >40m Lf 75-170mm Fl Dec-May 25-28mm Fr Dec-Feb 50-100mm

238 Scrub Ironwood (Python Tree)

Gossia bidwillii is one of several Gossia (prev. Austromyrtus) species found in Northern rainforests. The name Python tree is suggestive of the twisted nature of many of the trunks. The most distinctive feature of this tree is the smooth and colourful bark, often green with various shades of pink, brown and orange (Right and Left). The bark does flake (Left), but is often extremely smooth. On a cold morning, the dense wood stays cold and water condenses and runs off the trunks of the Ironwoods, while all the trees around are dry. This species will grow buttresses, but is commonly seen as a small tree. The shiny leaves are quite small, with elongated points. The tree at right has holes at the base which collect water. Such tree holes can be breeding sites for mosquitoes. Scrub Ironwood occurs from Cooktown to northern NSW.

Ht >25m Lf 25-105mm Fl Aug-Mar 4-10mm Fr Oct-May 4-10mm

239 Pencil Cedar (White Basswood)

Polyscias murrayi is one of several trees given the name Pencil Cedar. This is one of ten Australian species of Polyscias, all rather similar in their growth habit. (See Below) The large compound leaves, with between 8 and 30 pairs of leaflets, radiate from the top of the fast growing soft stem (Right). The edges of the leaves are minutely toothed, and the main leaf stalk is U shaped in cross-section. The tree will eventually grow to 30 metres. The flower head grows from the centre of the tree, and produces tiny green, white or cream flowers, followed by small flattened fruits that turn black/purple. These are eaten by many birds, Musky Rat-kangaroos, and Herbert River Ringtail Possums.

Pencil Cedar occurs from Cooktown in North Queensland to as far south as Victoria, but is restricted to Australia, as are most of the Polyscias species found here. This tree prefers the margins of rainforest, or disturbed areas within it.

Ht >30m   Lf 50-160mm   Fl Mar-May   Fr Jun-Oct 4-5mm

240 Celerywood (Celery Top)

Polyscias elegans grows a sapling with a single straight stem topped with an elegant rosette of branch like leaves up to a metre long (Right). The leaves are tripinnate, meaning a group of leaflets is arranged on a stem; those stems are arranged on larger stems; which are also arranged on yet larger stems to form a frond. The bark is pale and furrowed, smelling of celery if cut. Mature trees do branch but retain the airy spread of the large fern like leaves. Many small purple/black or maroon flowers are borne on heads above the canopy, followed by small purple/black berries in great profusion (Left) which are relished by many birds, including Bower Birds. The Green Cat Bird, with its cat like call, is one of these.

There are nine species of Polyscias in the rainforest, all bearing masses of small berries and large compound leaves. Celerywood grows from Cape York to northern NSW, and also in PNG.

Ht >30m   Lf 40-140mm   Fl Feb-Jul   Fr May-Nov 5-7mm

241 Ivory Basswood

Polyscias australiana is a fast growing small tree with large radiating compound leaves. The tree is notable for the size of the compound leaves (>1200mm) which have swellings where they clasp the trunk, and where the 7 to 21 leaflets attach. The small white or cream flowers are carried in a very loose head within the canopy,

and are followed by clusters of purple to black fruit. These fruits are eaten by many birds. Ivory Basswood occurs from Cape York to SE Qld, and also occurs in the NT and PNG. The tree commonly grows on the edge of rainforest, or in disturbed areas within rainforest. Golden Bower Birds often use the leaflets to decorate their bowers.

Ht >15m   Lf 70-240mm   Fl Jul-May   Fr Jul-Apr 5-10mm

242 Plasticine Tree (Lemon Aspen)

Acronychia aberrans belongs to a group of trees commonly known as 'Aspens', thirteen of which are found in the North Queensland rainforest and some of which, including the Plasticine tree, bear strongly lemon flavoured fruits. This small tree is found in the drier Mabi scrub of the Atherton Tableland, as well as in other high rainforest from the Windsor Tableland to Topaz. The twigs are squarish, with zig-zag ridges, and the leaves are simple, on longish stalks with a swelling at each end. The white or cream flowers with petals 8mm long, produce the green to yellow fruit with a strong lemon flavour, eaten by King Parrots, Spotted Catbirds, and Spectacled Flying Foxes. The oils making up about 1% of the Aspen fruits have beeen tested, and what is remarkable is the variety of components, with little overlap between species. The Lemon Aspen of commerce is a different species. This tree is also known as **Acid Berry**.

Ht >15m   Lf 60-290mm   Fl Feb-Apr >16mm   Fr Apr-Dec 30-35mm

243 Lime Berry (Butterfly Plant)

Micromelum minutum is a shrub or small tree which grows heads of perfumed small white, green or cream flowers that attract hordes of butterflies which feed from their nectar. The tree has somewhat drooping compound leaves, the 4-15 leaflets showing very unequal sides. The flowers are carried on panicles above the leaves, and are followed by bunches of orange, ripening to red, fruit. Growing from northern NSW (possibly extinct there) to Cape York, Lime Berry is found in SE Asia and the Pacific.

A Thai vegetable, it was used to treat skin ulcers and boils. Mahanine, an alkaloid derived from it, has strong antimutagenic and antimicrobial activity, and inhibits cell growth. Numerous chemicals, includ-

ing 12 coumarins, have been extracted from this tree.

Ht >9m   Lf 20-190mm   Fl Dec-Jun >6mm
Fr Jul-Feb 7-10mm

244 Bombax (Silk Cotton Tree)

Bombax ceiba is a tree which is impressive for its size, often overtopping the surrounding forest, and for its large, waxy red blooms. It is found in monsoon forest and the edges of rainforest, the tree at right beside the Kuranda Range road. The tree may be heavily buttressed as it ages, and may be covered with conical spines on the trunk. The leaves are often whorled, on long leaf stalks. The red, waxy flowers usually bloom when the tree is leafless. The 5 lobed pods contain large quantities of a low quality Kapok surrounding the seeds. Bombax occurs from Cape York to the Mulgrave River, also across northern Australia, through PNG, to Asia and India. In India it is a plantation timber, with traditional medicinal uses. The bark was used as an emetic and a tonic, and the gum treated dysentery. Young leaves and flowers are edible.

Photo - Krishna Buhler

Ht 25-45m Lf 60-220mm Fl Aug-Oct 60-90mm Fr Sep-Dec 80-120mm

245 Rubber Tree (Native Frangipani)

Cerbera manghas is a small tree which grows attractive bunches of white flowers with red centres. The name 'manghas' refers to the fruit which do somewhat resemble mangoes. The leaves are borne in whorls on the rather drooping branches. Flowering occurs throughout the year, and the fruits are green turning to red, of-

ten in pairs. Rubber Tree is found from Cape York to SE Qld, and also in the NT, and through PNG into Asia, sometimes growing as a mangrove. The white sap is extremely poisonous, and was used in hunting animals in Asia. The roots produce 3 cardenolides which have anti-cancer properties. A flammable oil can be produced from the kernals.

Ht >12m Lf 80-250mm Fl any month 20-35mm Fr Aug-May 60-80mm

246 Mulberry Leaved Stinger (Harmful Plant)

Dendrocnide photinophylla is related to the more dangerous Stinging Tree (no 1) but is described as 'mildly irritant'. It is also known as the **Shiny-leaved Stinger**. The tree usually has a grey bark and the leaves are large and shiny with prominent veins on longish leaf stalks. The leaves can have a serrated or smooth edge with stinging hairs usually on the underside. Tiny green or yellow-green flowers pro-

duce yellowish-green or white mulberry like fruit, each tiny sac containing a seed. Mulberry Leaved Stinger is found from Cooktown to near Sydney in NSW. The wood is fibrous and soft but Aboriginal people used the inner bark to make nets and lines. Tree Kangaroos enjoy the leaves as do many insects. It is a host plant for the White Nymph butterfly, the caterpillars of which hang off threads.

Ht >30m Lf 60-145mm Fl Jan-Aug Fr Feb-Jul

247 White Nettle (Butterfly Plant)

Pipturis argenteus is a small tree or shrub which is related to the Stinging Trees (nos 1 & 246) and it is sometimes known as the **False Stinger**, due to its lack of stinging hairs. The tree carries simple hairy leaves on long leaf stalks which may be red or pink. The similarity to nettles may be obvious. Small green, white or cream flowers produce interesting mulberry like white fruit which are eaten by numerous species of birds including Silvereyes and Lewin's Honeyeaters. The White Nettle

occurs from Cape York to Lismore in NSW, as well as in the NT, PNG and SE Asia. The Nettle family (Urticaceae) hosts many butterflies and the White Nettle is the food plant for the Yellow Admiral, White Nymph and the Speckled Lineblue butterflies in Australia.

Ht > 10m   Lf 30-170mm   Fl all year Fr Jan-Jun 4-6mm

248 Northern Olive

Chionanthus ramiflora is a white stemmed, often buttressed, tree of the rainforest and open forest (including close to beaches) which grows crops of purple or blue-black olive like fruit. The tree carries large simple leaves with longish leaf stalks and a marked midvein. Insignificant but fragrant white or cream flowers

precede the fruits which each contain a single large seed.

The Northern Olive, also known as the **Native Olive**, occurs from Cape York to Brisbane and also through PNG and the Solomon Islands into Asia. The fruits attract many birds, particularly Pigeons, and the leaves are eaten by Tree Kangaroos.

Ht >20m   Lf 50-220mm   Fl Oct-May
Fr   Jul-Feb 18-27mm

249 Camphor Laurel

Cinnamomum camphora is an introduced tree, native to Japan and China, now naturalised in rainforest and farmland from the Atherton Tableland, where it is often considered a weed, to Vic. The tree produces an attractive cabinet timber, growing to a large girth. 30kg of wood and leaves produces 1kg of camphor, used in perfumes and insecticides. In Asia there were many medicinal uses, including inhaling the oil fumes for lung conditions. Large quantities of the oil are poisonous. The shiny oval leaves on long stalks show a few distinct yellow veins. The smell of the crushed leaf is unmistakable. Small white or cream flowers produce black single seeded fruits which are eaten, and spread, by many birds. Camphor Laurel was introduced into Australia as a shade tree in 1822, and is now a serious weed of creek and river banks here, and overseas. A single tree can produce 100,000 seeds a year. This is an attractive turning timber.

Ht >20m   Lf 30-100mm   Fl Aug-Oct   Fr Jan-Mar 8-9mm

250 Tingletongue

Dinosperma erythrococcum is a medium sized rainforest and dry forest tree, found from Cape York to the Clarence River in NSW. It is one of four species of Dinosperma which are found only in Australia. It occurs in the dryer Mabi rainforest at Halloran's Hill in Atherton. The tree bears compound leaves with 3 or 5 leaflets with 10 to 17 pairs of lateral veins, and swollen leaf stalks. Small, fragrant, green, white or cream flowers produce the bright orange or red fruits which are usually in pairs. The fleshy fruits become wrinkled and disintegrate, leaving the metallic blue to black

seeds attached to the plant. These are eaten by King Parrots. Tingletongue's common name comes from chewing the bark or leaf which will cause a numbing or tingling effect. The leaves are known to contain four types of oil.

Ht >25m   Lf 23-130mm   Fl Apr-Oct
Fr Oct-Jun 4-9mm

251 Yellow Mahogany

Dysoxylum parasiticum is a 'cauliflorous' tree, bearing flowers and fruit on the trunk and branches. The flowers (Below) are right at ground level. Osbeck, a student of Linnaeus, the great cataloguer of the living world, mistakenly thought these must belong to a parasite, hence the scientific name. The tree may be buttressed

and has compound leaves of 13-20 leaflets which may be densely hairy. The flowers are fragrant, white or cream, and up to 20mm long. They are carried on bumps on the trunk or branches, where the fruit later develop. The orange-brown capsules occur in bunches and attract birds such as the Metallic Starling which eat the red arils. Yellow Mahogany occurs from Cape York to Ingham and through PNG and SE Asia into Taiwan. In Bali it was considered a "tree of the Gods" and the faintly fragrant wood was used in shrines.

Ht > 27m   Lf 40-250mm   Fl May-Sep >35mm   Fr Nov-Feb 20-40mm

252 Spurwood

Dysoxylum pettigrewianum is notable for the large protrusions on the buttresses (shown here) and also for broad flanges in the branches. The tree bears large compound leaves of 7-15 overlapping leaflets. Fragrant white or cream flowers produce orange or brown warty fruits containing 1-4 brownish-red and white seeds. These are eaten by Cassowaries, which eat the whole fruit, or Metallic Starlings, which remove the seeds. Spurwood occurs from Cooktown to Paluma. It is also found in PNG, the Solomon Islands and SE Asia. It is one of 14 species of Dysoxylum found in the Qld rainforests, many of which produce valuable timber. The red brown timber from this species is pleasant to smell unlike others in the family.

Ht >35m   Lf 50-270mm   Fl Dec-Jan   Fr Oct-Mar 30-45mm

253 Coral Tree

Erythrina variegata is a showy tree with vivid red flowers on bare branches while the tree is wintering. (One cultivar does not drop its leaves, though.) The tree has thorny stems, and the trunk is pithy and light. The compound leaves comprise 3 leaflets on a long leaf stalk. The pea like flowers are striking and produce hooked brown to black pods containing several seeds. The Coral Tree is found from Cape

York to Gladstone, usually near sea level, and also occurs in the NT, and throughout the Pacific, Asia and Africa. It is a good forage tree for cattle, produces fence posts that grow, and is suitable for paper pulp. In India it had many medicinal uses, including against parasites and worms. A legume, it is a good green manure plant.

Ht >25m   Lf 80-200mm   Fl Jul-Nov >75mm
Fr Jun-Feb 70-300mm

254 Northern Brush Mahogany

Geissois biagiana is a hard to pronounce but easy to recognise rainforest tree. The leaflets are arranged in threes, at the end of a long leaf stalk, but it is the leaf-like stipules that form small butterflies at the junction with the twig, that are distinctive. The tree produces small white or cream flowers followed by banana like bunches of fruit capsules eaten by Double-eyed Fig-parrots. Northern Brush Mahogany, also known as **Red Carabeen**, occurs from Mt Spurgeon to Cardwell, and is one of two Australian species. It is famous for the brilliant red of its new growth and for the large buttresses produced by the tree. The timber is used for joinery. The spikes seen on the leaves in the photograph are due to insect attack.

Ht >33m   Lf 60-280mm   Fl Nov-Dec&Apr   Fr Jan-Apr 8-12mm

255 Blush Silky Oak (Wingleaf Silky Oak)

Gevuina bleasdalei is the latest of a series of names for this rainforest tree belonging to the Proteaceae, a family which has ancient ancestry. This is the only Australaian species, while the only other two species are found in PNG and South America, suggesting a Gondwana connection. The plant is most likely to be noticed due to its large compound leaves with winged sections on the leaf stalks between the leaflets. The tree occurs in highland rainforest, and the compound leaves are comprised of from 3-19 leaflets which have toothed margins and may be covered with rusty to crimson hairs when young.

Blush Silky Oak is found in a limited area of North Queensland, from Mt Lewis to the ranges inland of Mackay. The seeds are eaten and spread by Cassowaries. The flowers are white or cream, yellowish inside, rusty or pinkish hairy outside, and occur at any time of year. The fruits were unknown until recently and are blue or black with thin flesh over a large seed.

Ht >24m   Lf 30-200mm   Fl any month 7-12mm   Fr Nov-Mar 15-25mm

256 Brown Boxwood (Butterfly Plant)

Homalium circumpinnatum is a lowland rainforest tree which produces small shuttlecock shaped flowers, inspiring it's alternative common name of **Shuttlecock Flower**. The photographs, taken on the Kuranda Range road, show the buds. The tree may be buttressed, and bears a dense and rather untidy foliage of shiny, toothed leaves. The small green, white or cream flowers have an unpleasant scent, but attract many butterflies. The fruits are white or cream and have the wilted flowers attached. Brown Boxwood occurs between Iron Range and Proserpine. It is one of five rainforest species of Homalium and is the host plant for the Swordgrass Brown butterfly. It is a desirable garden tree, of modest size and able to attract butterflies.

Ht >32m Lf 50-100mm   Fl Nov-Aug   Fr Feb 5-6mm

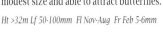

257 Noahdendron (Primitive Plant)

Noahdendron nicholasii is a primitive plant of the rainforest at Noah Creek near Cape Tribulation. It can be seen from the Marrdja boardwalk or at the Cairns Botanic Gardens. Of the 19 families of primitive flowering plants identified worldwide, 13 are found in the Daintree Rainforest. Some, like the Noahdendron, are found nowhere else. This does not mean that Australia was home to the flowering plants but that this area retains a unique collection of these primitive plants in refugia, areas that survived climate change, sea level changes, vulcanism, and so on, over many millions of years. Noahdendron can be recognised by the leaf-like stipules where the leaf stalks join the thin stems. The flowers are pink or red, hanging in a bundle, and the fruits are bundles of brown capsules, each 2 lobed, that are woody and covered with rusty hairs.

Ht >10m Lf 120-300mm Fl Jul-Sep Fr Nov-Jun 10mm on >100mm spike

258 Idiot Fruit (Primitive Plant)

Idiospermum australiense is the most famous of the primitive plants found in North Queensland. First discovered south of Cairns, it was believed extinct until found in 1971 near Noah Creek where it had poisoned cattle. It belongs to an ancient family previously known only as fossils. The tennis ball sized fruits are poisonous to all known animals and birds. Possibly extinct animals, from the megafauna, once spread these fruits. Uniquely they produce 3 or 4 seed leaves, unlike all other plants on earth, and can produce multiple shoots per seed. Three alkaloids, including idiospermuline, which is able to disrupt nerve transmission in the brain, have been extracted from the fruits, with possible medicinal uses. The trees are not rare in the tiny areas they inhabit. They bear pink, red or orange fragrant flowers.

Ht >25m Lf 100-240mm Fl Jun-Oct Fr Jun-Feb

259 Stockwellia (Ancestral Plant)

Stockwellia quadrifida is an ancestral plant recently discovered in North Queensland. In this case it possibly represents an ancestor of Australia's dominant Eucalypts and is a close relative to Turpentine (see no 389). Stockwellias are big trees, some with huge buttresses. The leaves are simple. New growth is bright pink with

the leading two leaves standing clear on the shoot. Flowers are from green through white to pink. The fruits resemble two or three large gum nuts fused together at right angles, and are eaten by White Cockatoos. Stockwellia trees occur in two main stands, one near Boonjee, the other on the flanks of Mt Bellenden Kerr. They are named after Victor Stockwell, the forest ranger who discovered them.

Ht >40m Lf 50-145mm Fl Nov-Dec Fr May-Dec

260 Paperbark Satinash

Syzygium papyraceum is a distinctive tree of upland rainforest due to its thin papery bark which can glow orange amongst the drab trunks of other trees. The tree bears simple leaves and is usually buttressed. Often the trunk is poorly shaped. The fragrant flowers may be white, cream, pink or purple, and produce purple berries with the calyx forming a cross on the end of each. Paperbark Satinash occurs from the Windsor Tableland, inland from Mossman, to near Mackay. It is not listed as a timber tree, though possibly milled in small quantities. The tree has entered the nursery trade for the flowers, with a spicy perfume, showy purple fruit (which may be edible - do not eat fruits which you are not sure of - they may be poisonous) and the striking bark. Vines do not easily attach to this bark.

Ht >35m   Lf 60-130mm   Fl Sep-Nov   Fr Dec-Feb 25-33mm

261 Rough Trema

Trema orientalis is distinguishable as a young tree by the thin foliage borne on thin looping branches. The tree may develop buttresses. The finely toothed narrow leaves taper to a fine point and are hairy or sandpapery on top and densely hairy underneath. Tiny greenish flowers are borne from Oct to Mar and small purple to black clusters of fruit follow. These fruits are eaten by Cassowaries, Figbirds, and Satin Bowerbirds. Two species of Trema occur in Australia, both known as **Poison Peach**. Rough Trema occurs from Cape York to Bundaberg. It is widespread across the pacific, through Asia and in Africa. It is a weed in Hawaii, but used widely in Asia for land reclamation as it colonises poor soil and fixes nitrogen. In Africa it had many medicinal uses and was an insect repellent and butterfly host. String was made from the bark and the leaves were eaten as spinach. It was used as cattle fodder and for charcoal.

Ht >30m   Lf 40-200mm   Fl Oct-Mar   Fr Jan-Mar 3-5mm

262 Orange Jacket (Butterfly Plant)

Xylopia maccreae is most likely to be noticed when it is fruiting. The bunches of yellow brown, slightly hairy fruits are unremarkable, but when they split they reveal light blue or grey arils suspended under a red or orange canopy - a striking sight. The tree has hairy stems and may be buttressed. The simple leaves are smooth on top; densely hairy underneath. The flowers are quite large, with 6 white, cream or yellow petals. The seeds inside the bluish arils on the fruit are black. Orange Jacket occurs from Cape York to near Mackay. It belongs to the Custard Apple family and is a host for the Green Spotted Triangle butterfly.

Ht >25m   Lf 40-150mm   Fl Jan-Mar&Aug >22mm   Fr Oct-May 35-50mm

263 Thorny Yellowwood (Butterfly Plant)

Zanthoxylum ovalifolium is a small treee that grows on the margin of rainforest, often as a shrub, with barnacle shaped thorns on the trunk. The tree can reach 6 metres in height and occurs as separate male and female plants. The compound leaves are made up of from 1 to 3 leaflets, either smooth edged or toothed. The crushed leaves smell of oranges. The small white or cream flowers are fragrant and are followed by red or maroon fruits which also have a strong orange perfume if bruised. Each fruit contains 1 or 2 black seeds, which are reported to be peppery. Thorny Yellowwood occurs from the Bloomfield river to Ravenshoe, a quite small area of North Queensland, but is also found through PNG into Asia. In Asia it has had many medicinal uses, and modern research has focussed on its volatile oils, the antibacterial compounds in the fruits, and the alkaloids from the bark. It is the host plant for the Ambrax Swallowtail butterfly and the wood has been used as a curiosity by wood turners due to its yellow colour.

Ht >6m   Lf 40-170mm   Fl Dec-Mar   Fr Mar-Oct 6-7mm

264 Daintree Penda

Lindsayomyrtus racemoides is a lowland rainforest tree that attracts attention (notably about July) when the pale mauve to bright purple new growth appears. There are many of these trees visible at the Mossman Gorge at this time. The tree grows large simple leaves with the new growth hanging in limp whorls. The fragrant flowers are cream or white and have 5 petals. Flowers grow in profusion with prominent yellow stamens. The fruits are green capsules which may be 1-3 lobed. These tear open as the seeds expand. This tree may have a future as an ornamental tree in the tropics. Daintree Penda is the single species from its genus and is found only in a small area from Cooktown to Babinda in North Queensland. It also occurs in PNG, and in Indonesia (the Moluccas).

Ht >30m Lf 90-240mm Fl Oct-Dec 8-10mm Fr Dec-Feb 23-33mm

265 Turn-in-the-Wind

Mallotus paniculatus is a shrub or small tree of rainforest edges with characteristic elongated leaves, drawn out to a fine tip and carried on long leaf stalks. The leaves are simple and may have smooth or toothed edges, with 1 or 2 flat black glands on top near the leaf base. The leaves may be smooth or rusty hairy on top; densely hairy on the whitish undersides and flutter in a breeze. Tiny green, white or yellow flowers are borne in branching heads (the meaning of 'paniculatus'), followed by white or cream 4-6mm capsules covered with rubbery bristles and containing two or three brown or black shiny seeds. Turn-in-the-Wind occurs from Cape York to near Mackay, as well as in Asia. It is a common regrowth tree of disturbed sites. In Asia it is used to treat ulcers of the skin and for paper production.

Ht >10m Lf 40-190mm Fl Sep-Jul Fr any month

266 Hypsophila

Hypsophila dielsiana is a shrub or small tree of upland rainforest - Hypsophila meaning "high loving". While the glossy leaves with looping veins are rather distinctive, together with the pink-purple leaf stalks, identification is easily verified by checking the stalk to which the leaves are attached. A small ridge zig-zags along this stalk from one leaf base to the next. The tree will most probably be observed as a shrub such as in the photograph (Right) taken on Mt Sorrow. The leaves are simple or have rounded teeth. Flowers are red, pink or purple followed by three valved capsules somewhat resembling Flindersia fruits (see no 220) containing a number of brown seeds embedded in red or orange arils. These fruits have also been described as Gherkin like and hang on long stems, as do the flowers.

Hypsophila is one of only two species within this genus. Both are found only in Australia, between Cooktown and Tully.

Ht > 10m   Lf 70-210mm   Fl Feb-Nov 9mm   Fr Nov-Aug 55-100mm

267 Apricot Myrtle

Pilidiostigma tropicum grows as a shrub or small tree with an irregular straggly habit. The tree bears simple leaves with an undulating margin and veins forming loops well inside the margins. The flowers are composed of 5 white, cream or pink petals. The fruits are berries which turn purple or black as they ripen and are eaten by many bird species as well

as by Spectacled Flying Foxes. Apricot Myrtle occurs only in Australia in a rather limited area from Tinaroo on the Atherton Tablelands to Paluma north of Townsville. It has been introduced into cultivation and is a source of anti-bacterial compounds.

Ht >20m   Lf 40-90mm   Fl Sep-Dec >14mm   Fr Dec-Mar 12-22mm

268 Davidson's Plum

Davidsonia pruriens is the only one of three Australian species of this genus to be found in the Northern rainforests. It is notable for the large and hairy compound leaves with even the main leaf stalk bearing leaf like protrusions between leaflets. The edges of the leaflets are toothed and both sides are covered in hairs. The large blackish purple fruit also tend to be covered with fine irritant hairs, though some strains without hairs have been selected for cultivation. The fruit has a powdery 'bloom' on the surface and contains two strangely shaped seeds, only one of which is usually fertile. Though generally too tart to eat raw, the fruit makes attractive jam and wine, and is grown as a domestic fruit. The tree grows more than one trunk, usually of unequal lengths, giving it an informal look. All three species of Davidsonia are found only in Australia, this one from Cooktown to Cardwell. It is reasonably common near Kuranda and can be seen on the Jum Rum Creek walk there. Aboriginal people ate the fruit which has been described as the best Australian native fruit and their name for it, **Ooray**, is still in use.

Ht >18m   Lf 50-460mm (Compound leaf >1500mm) Fl any month Fr any month 30-55mm

SEEDLINGS

269 Blue Umbrella

Macklinaya confusa may be encountered in rainforest as a seedling or small shrub. It grows to a large shrub. The seedling (Left) shows the whorls of usually 5 -7 leaflets, with serrated edges, and occasionally lobed. Flowers (green, white, cream, red or purple) and seeds are held in a complex structure above the plant (Right). The fruits are variable in colour - reddish, blue, purple or black, about 10mm across, and may be two lobed. Blue Umbrella is one of two Australian species and occurs from Cape York to Hinchinbrook Island near Cardwell, from sea level to mountain tops. The flesh of the fruits is eaten by Eclectus Parrots, Bower Birds and Cassowaries.

Ht >6m   Lf 100-210mm   Fl any month   Fr Jul-Jan 8-13mm

270 Pepper Tree (Primitive Plant)

Tasmannia insipida is one of the living fossils of the rainforest representing an ancient family with only Southern Hemisphere relatives. A close relative is used in Tasmania to produce a native pepper, hence the common name. The fuits, often purple or black, contain seeds which are reported to be peppery to taste. The leaves taper into a short leaf stalk which can be bright pink (Right). The radiating leaves grow on the ends of the branches of an untidy shrub. The green, white or cream flowers are followed by cream, red, purple or black berries. Pepper tree grows in SE Australia and at higher altitudes (eg Kahlpahlim Rock) in North Queensland. The plant contains polygodial, a potent antifungal compound.

Ht >5m   Lf 60-210mm   Fl Apr-Oct   Fr Sep-Apr 10-20mm

271 Rose Silky Oak (Primitive Plant)

Placospermum coriaceum is the only plant of this genus in the world and comes from a restricted area in North Queensland. It is the most primitive member of the large and important Proteaceae family that has 1100 Australian species. It grows to a large tree with a soft pink wood that is very attractive. The young leaves (Left) are deeply lobed, but slightly older leaves may be simple, elongated, and shiny (Right). The fruits are brown pods containing about 20 heart shaped seeds stacked together like a pack of cards. 'Coriaceum' means 'leathery' and refers to the leaves.

Rose Silky Oak is found in the limited area between Cooktown and Mt Bellenden Ker, mostly at higher altitudes. The attractive pink tips to young leaves, and the dense racemes of slender pink flowers make it an attractive but large garden plant. The soft timber has been milled.

Ht >30m   Lf 65-250mm(mature)   Fl Sep-Jan   Fr Mar-Oct 28-43mm

272 Red Oak (Primitive Plant)

Carnarvonia araliifolia is another single species genus found only in Far North Queensland (See no 271). This plant will grow into a 30m tree, with interesting woody fruits like the beak of a big bird. The compound leaves are made up of from 3 to 20 leaflets which may be toothed or smooth edged (Right). Masses of pink, white or cream hairy flowers are followed by the woody fruits containing 1 or 2 winged seeds. Of the 19 families of primitive flowering plants worldwide, 13 are found in the North Queensland rainforest, and two nowhere else. Red Oak occurs only between Cooktown and Ingham. The rich brown heartwood was used for furniture, veneer and woodware.

Ht >30m   Lf 45-200mm   Fl Nov-May   Fr Jul-Mar 40-50mm

273 Brown Silky Oak

Darlingia darlingiana is a tree which is restricted to Far North Queensland. There are two species, this one found from Cooktown to Paluma. The leaves (Left) can be simple or lobed as shown and up to half a metre in length. The full grown tree can be buttressed and produces a pale pink-brown, straight grained, extremely durable timber useful for joinery, furniture and plywood. The ostentatious, nectar-rich flowers on long spikes attract birds, and make this an attractive garden plant. It contains 'darlingene', an alkaloid, that may cause muscle contraction.

Ht >30m   Lf 70-500mm   Fl May-Nov   Fr Nov-Jan 45-70mm

274 Native Holly

Alyxia ilicifolia is a most attractive shrub with hard shiny leaves, that are spiky like Holly ('ilicifolia' means 'Holly-like leaves'). If broken, the stems exude a white, sticky sap. The photograph (Below) is from Kahlpahlim Rock where the shrub is common. The leaves are considerably larger than the closely related Chain Fruit (no 327) being up to 150 mm long. There are about 50 pairs of lateral veins almost at right angles to the centre vein of the leaf, and distinct on the leaf underside. Fruit are orange berries, sometimes growing end to end like beads on a necklace. The white flowers (sometimes cream, pink or purple) are fragrant, and occur throughout the year, as do the fruits. Native Holly is found between Cooktown and Ingham in Far North Qld, commonly at high altitude, though it can grow at lower levels.

Ht >5m   Lf 40-150mm   Fl 8-12mm   Fr 11-23mm

275 Mountain Kauri (Primitive Plant)

Agathis atropurpurea is also known as the **Blue**, **Purple** or **Black Kauri**, referring to the striking mulberry coloured trunk (Left). Some beautiful large specimens (>50m) occur near the top of Kahlpahlim Rock, where this species almost forms a monoculture in parts. The leaves (30-70mm) are a bright green, with lime green tips (foliage at bottom of photo, Left) and form an attractive canopy. Bark is shed as scales, towards the end of the year, and new bark is especially striking in colour. The white sap can be used as a fire lighter, burning even in wet conditions with a smoky flame. Fruits are similar to the closely related Kauri Pine (See no 185) though smaller. These trees are found on only a few high peaks from Mt Pieter Botte to

Mt Bartle Frere, above 750 metres altitude, growing on infertile granite soils. The sap is a source of agatholic acid, and the timber was used for ply and guitar bodies. Most trees that were accessible were heavily logged before World Heritage listing.

276 Tree Waratah

Alloxylon wickhamii is a rainforest tree, usually found at high altitudes, that grows striking pink or pink-red flowers. Like its close relative, the Queensland Waratah, it occurs only in a small area of North Queensland, between Cooktown and the Atherton Tableland. Tree Waratah is one of only four species of Alloxylon world wide, three of which occur in Australia. Tree Waratah can grow to 30 metres, and may be buttressed. The leaves (60-240mm) are simple, with a swelling on the leaf stalk. The showy flowers (20-40mm) (Oct-Dec) are held upright at the tips of the branches. They are followed by brown fruits (55-120mm) (Aug-Oct) each containing about 10 winged seeds.

Tree Waratah has been examined as a potential cut flower export crop.

PALMS

277 Grey Palm

Oraniopsis appendiculata is a palm found mostly at higher elevations in rainforest. Grey Palm occurs from Cooktown to Tully. Looking not unlike a small coconut palm, its foliage tends to a silvery or bluish hue on the undersides of the fronds. The largest numbers of these palms are to be seen on Mt Lewis, but there are a number beside the track to Kahlpahlim Rock. It produces masses of orange fruit. This palm is the only species in its family, and is found only in Australia. Its closest relatives are palms in Madagascar and the Andean Wax Palms of South America, providing evidence for the ancient super-continent of Pangea.

Ht >25m   Lf 140-200mm on fronds >1m   Fl Mar-Aug 8mm   Fr Nov-Mar 27-35mm

278 Solitaire Palm (Butterfly Plant)

Ptychosperma elegans is well known around the world as a cultivated palm. It is a graceful palm with a smooth slender trunk showing prominent rings where the fronds attached. These are solitary, not clumping, palms, as the common name suggests. Solitaire palms grow to 15m, with fronds to 3m, made up of from 40 to 60 leaflets, and produce masses of green, white or cream flowers followed by bunches of red fruit. The fruits are eaten by many birds, including Cassowaries, Pied Imperial-pigeons, fruit-doves, Figbirds, and Lewin's Honeyeaters. This palm is also the food plant of the Orange Palmdart butterfly. It is found only in Queensland from Cape York to Fraser Island.

These attractive palms can be viewed on the Mt Whitfield walk next to the Cairns Botanic Gardens in Collins Avenue. The photograph is of palms in the Gardens. Although not yet a weed overseas, it is listed as an invasive species in Florida.

Ht >15m   Lf 250-900mm (on fronds to 3m)   Fl Jan&Jul 8-10mm   Fr Apr-Nov&Jan 12-20mm

279 Alexandra Palm

Archontophoenix alexandrae is one of the most familiar of the Australian palms, now widely planted around the world. This solitary palm can reach 30 metres in height, with fronds up to 4.5 metres long, bearing between 120 and 160 leaflets. The upper side of these leaflets is shiny, while underneath they are whitish, or clothed in silvery scales. The flowerstalk is up to 800mm long, bearing hundreds of white or cream, three petalled flowers, at any time of year. The red fruits may also occur at any time of the year.

The Alexander Palm occurs between Cape Melville, north of Cooktown, and Gladstone in SE Qld. It favours low swampy environments, and is favoured for wet sites as a garden plant. In Hawaii it has become an invasive weed. A form from Mt. Elliott near Townsville has a thicker 'stepped' trunk. Mature trees usually have a thickened base, up to 300mm through. The clean leaf fall and the green top to the trunk have added to the popularity of this palm in cultivation.

Ht >30m   Lf 250-750mm (on fronds >4.5m)   Fl any month 6-7mm   Fr any month 8-14mm

280 Fishtail Lawyer Cane

Calamus caryotoides has fronds ending in a distinctive fish tail. It has thin stems, and the tendrils, though short, can be as fine as a cotton thread, making them very hard to see. Even so, they are just as strong as their relatives (See nos 2-4), and quite capable of tearing skin and clothing. The fruits are 8-13mm golden spheres. They develop on what appear to be modified tendrils following three petalled green, yellow or orange flowers. Between six and twelve leaflets make up each frond, with fine spines along the margins. This species grows only from Iron Range to Ingham.

Ht > 6m   Lf 100-240mm   Fl Nov-Apr   Fr Mar-Dec

281 Minor Walking Stick Palm

Linospadix minor is a small palm with a prominent fishtail leaf, which grows showy pendants of bright orange or red fruits. The palm can reach 5 metres, though is usually much less, and may form clumps. The compound leaves carry from 2 to 14 leaflets with the terminal leaflets joined to form a fishtail. Small green, white or cream flowers form on a spike which goes on to produce the fruits which can be seen throughout the year. Some plants produce orange seeds, while others produce red. Minor Walking Stick Palm is found from the coast near Coen to Tully and also occurs in PNG on the Fly River. These palms are very variable in leaf shape and the number of plants growing together. Cassowaries eat the fruits. The Minor Walking Stick Palm is a widely grown ornamental palm.

Ht >5m   Lf 70-435mm (on fronds >1100mm)   Fl Jul-Sep   Fr 8-18mm

282 Myola Palm (Myolan Alexandra Palm)

Archontophoenix myolensis resembles and is related to the Alexandra palm (no 279) which is found from Cape Melville north of Cooktown to Gladstone in SE Qld. This species, though is found in a very restricted area near Myola, west of Kuranda. The trees grow to 20m with fronds up to 4m long, bearing from 136 to 142 leaflets which are whitish or silvery on the undersides. White or cream, three petalled flowers are borne from May to Jul, and the fruit ripen to red between Dec and Mar. One distinguishing feature of this palm is the third order branching of the flower stalks.

Palms probably evolved in western Gondwana and reached the Australian land mass about 100 million years ago. They are amongst the earliest forms of flowering plants. Endemic species developed after Australia separated from Gondwana, and more recently Asian species have entered from the north, resulting in a rich diversity of palms occurring in North Queensland.

Ht >20m   Lf 500-1100mm (on fronds >4m)   Fl Mar-Jul 7-8mm   Fr Dec-Mar 14-21mm

TREE FERNS

283 Rebecca's Tree Fern

Cyathea rebeccae is a slender dark trunked tree fern, often found along roadsides in rainforest. It can grow to 7 metres in height, with a trunk diameter of 100mm. The fronds can reach 3 metres in length and carry dark green shiny leaflets with serrated margins. The untidy trunks can sucker from the base.

The Cyathea genus contains about 800 species worldwide, of which only 11 species are found in Australia, 7 in Far North Queensland. Tree ferns have not changed much since they evolved some 325m years ago.

Rebecca's Tree Fern occurs in central and north Queensland, and in Malaysia. It has proven popular as a garden or indoor plant, and will grow easily even in Southern states provided it is protected from frost. It makes an excellent tub plant.

284 Scaly Tree Fern (Lacy Tree Fern)

Cyathea cooperi is the only local tree fern that thrives in full sun. It is widely grown in gardens for that reason, and is also common in the area. Some attractive examples are growing on the Kuranda Range beside the Kennedy Highway. Scaly Tree Fern can reach heights of 12m with a canopy as wide. The slender trunks (>150mm) show distinctive oval leaf scars (Left) and are thickened at the base. Being vigorous growers, and sun tolerant, these tree ferns are grown world wide wherever it is warm enough. They are a weed in Hawaii.

Tree ferns reproduce by shedding tiny spores from sori on the leaves. The spore develops into a small heart shaped thallus. The male cells at the point burst when wet, and the sperm migrate to the female cells at the notch, there developing into a new plant. They also reproduce asexually by rhizomes.

285 Tree Fern

Cyathea woollsiana is a slender rainforest species with broad arching fronds. It can be identified by the green base to new fronds, and the long curved bristle-like 'scales' at the base of mature fronds. It will grow to a similar size to Rebecca's Tree Fern (no 283), with a slender trunk (>150mm). The fronds are soft and pale green in young plants, shiny green in older plants.

This tree fern is found in NE Qld, usually in mountainous areas. Tree Ferns are found throughout Australia's rainforest, in some places forming the dominant vegetation. In North Queensland it is unusual to find masses of tree ferns, but they are common on old logging roads and in damp areas such as gullies. Aboriginal people ate the growing point in this species, breaking open the crown and rinsing the tannins from the soft starch-rich heart, which tastes like turnip.

FERNS

286 Basket Fern

Drynaria rigidula grows on trees as an epiphyte (Left), but also grows on rocks, when it is known as a lithophyte. These ferns grow two kinds of leaves. The 'nest' leaves are wide and short, near the base of the fronds, collecting leaf litter for nutrients and shading the hairy rhizomes, or roots. The fronds themselves bear the sori, the fern's spore cases, and can be one and a half metres long. This species is one of three in northern Australia, extending as far south as northern NSW, and north into SE Asia. When found in open forest the clumps are smaller, possibly due to fire. It is widely cultivated, and the form 'whitei' has branching leaflets.

287 Bird's Nest Fern

Asplenium australasicum is another epiphyte common in rainforest. The ferns can grow very large and encircle the tree. It is also found growing on rocks, and has become a familiar garden plant throughout the world, since it is easy to grow and the roots are relatively small. Very large specimens grow in Southern Queensland but in the tropics the fronds are rarely longer than a metre. In the photo (Top Right), you can see the lines of sori on the leaves, towards the apex. These are the structures that produce tiny spores, which blow away to start new plants. They are the equivalent of seed for ferns which are more primitive than the flowering plants. The leaves catch litter and this helps feed the plant. The closely related *Asplenium nidus* (Left) has a very raised midrib.

288 Northern Elkhorn

Platycerium hillii like the ferns above, is an epiphyte. Unlike parasites, epiphytes do not harm their hosts, using them for support so that they are able to gain access to the sunlight at the top of the canopy. The plant at right was growing in windswept ridge vegetation while the one at top left was in a She-oak tree beside a river and you can see the dark patches of spores under the tips of the fronds. The plant (below, Left) is growing on the trunk of a Palm Cycad. Elkhorns are common in rainforest, from Cape York to Ingham. The 'nest leaves' (100-250mm) form pots for the humus the plant feeds on. They are light green to brown, and smooth. The true leaves divide at the ends and in the cultivated form 'Cobra' are twisted. It pays to stop from time to time when walking in rainforest to inspect the canopy for the variety of striking epiphytes that are visible.

289 King Fern (Primitive)

Angiopteris evecta is reputed to be the world's largest fern, with fronds up to 5 metres long. The fern (Right), on the Clohesy River road, has lost a number of fronds, exposing the thick butt. Pigs attack and eat the starchy rhizomes. This is a very primitive fern similar to fossils found in Upper Paleozoic rocks (up to 300m years old - and the source of most coal) on all continents. The fronds are kept erect by 'turgor', the pressure of the sap in the cells.

It is not easy to discriminate this fern from the **Potato Fern**, also found here, but Potato ferns tend to grow in clumps and stain blue/purple when cut. King ferns occur from Madagascar through tropical Asia to NE Australia and the W Pacific. The photo at left shows the knobbly butt, with ear like swellings at the base of the fronds. This fern is now a weed in parts of Hawaii.

290 Filmy Fern

Hymenophyllum walleri is a delicate fern of high rainforest areas where constant moisture protects the fronds, which are only a single cell thick. This specimen (Right) was on Kahlpahlim Rock. This is a large and complex group, with the number of Australian species listed by different authorities varying from 19 to 46! This species is found only in Queensland from the Lamb Range near Cairns to the Eungella Range near Mackay. It is a neat, compact filmy fern, found usually in rainforest, growing on trees or amongst the roots of other epiphytes. The fronds (>50mm) are usually broad and the sori that carry the spores are on the ends of the lobes, and wider than the lobes. The stems are covered with short dense hairs. The fronds are bipinnate, meaning that the branching leaflets are carried on stems that themselves are carried on a branching stem.

Most of Australia's filmy ferns grow in northeast Queensland.

291 Fern (Nephrolepis)

Nephrolepis hirsutula is one of several species from this family in North East Queensland. This is a hardy species growing on rocky banks at Crystal Cascades, where it forms large masses (Left). The fronds are coarse and somewhat brittle, dark green but tending to bleach in exposed areas. The spores (Below, Right) are located in kidney shaped structures called sori on the backs of the fronds, close to the edges. The fronds are tufted and erect or arching (>1.8m), pinnate (with the leaflets arranged each side of a midrib), with irregular teeth on each pointed leaflet. The first tooth is often greatly elongated (Right).

292 Filmy Maidenhair

Adiantum diaphanum is a beautiful Maidenhair Fern that favours wet banks, stream verges and rainforest. It will tolerate very dark conditions. The main stem is thin, smooth and black, and the leaflets carry between five and eight sori each, containing the spores. Although it appears delicate, it is actually quite easy to cultivate. It is growing at Crystal Cascades.

Adiantums are distinguished by the fan shape of the lealets, and the polished black or purple colour of the stems. They have been widely cultivated and used as pot plants, some being quite drought tolerant. There are about 200 species world wide, mostly from South America, with about nine from Australia. This species is found in rainforest areas in Qld and NSW with a few rare specimens in Vic. It extends to China, Fiji and Norfolk Island.

293 Rough Maidenhair

Adiantum hispidulum occurs in many forms throughout rainforest and even in open rocky situations, where it survives drought by curling the fronds. New growth can be a delicate pink colour. This is a tough and wiry fern that does well in cultivation. The fronds of this species are bipinnate or tripinnate, light to dark green, with minute white hairs. It varies greatly in form, making identification more difficult. There are from six to fourteen sori, bearing the spores, on each leaflet. It is widespread in Australia, and extends to NZ, the Pacific islands, Asia and Africa. This plant was growing near the boardwalk at the Cairns Botanic Gardens .

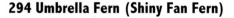

294 Umbrella Fern (Shiny Fan Fern)

Sticherus flabellatus forms umbrella like layers of fronds, dark green above, light below. It is a fern that likes to grow near water. The Rhizome is long-creeping and wiry, with fronds up to 2 metres long, but usually under 1 metre. A compact variety is found on Mountains in north Qld. The simple leaflets are at an angle of about 45 degrees to the central stem. The sori containing the spores are in single rows either side of the midrib.

There are about 100 species of Sticherus worldwide, with only three found in Australia. This species is found along the east coast as far south as Victoria, and also in PNG, New Caledonia and New Zealand.

It is slow to grow in cultivation, and resents disturbance. The roots must be kept moist at all times.

295 Dwarf Hare's Foot Fern

Humata repens is a small attractive fern of rainforest margins, shown here from the Mossman Gorge. The dark triangular fronds are leathery and up to 200mm long. The veins are conspicuous and the sori, containing the spores, are found in small indentations near the tips of the lobes, where they are covered by a papery hood. The runners or rhizomes, from which the fronds rise on long slender stems, are often buried in the moss and lichens. Dwarf Hare's Foot Fern occurs in NE Qld, and has been introduced as a garden plant into other areas where it can be slow growing in cool climates.

296 Coral Fern (Primitive Plant)

Lycopodiella cernua (prev Lycopodium cernuum) is a striking and attractive fern often found in road cuttings in full sun, like this photograph of plants seen near Kuranda. This is the most vigorous of about 17 Australian species, many of which are known as Tassell Ferns and hang down from tree trunks. The stems of this species are wiry and scramble over banks and other vegetation. The leaves are small, about 6mm long, and scattered along the stems. Spores are borne on strobili, cone shaped structures found at the ends of small branches. There are no fronds as such. Coral Fern is not a true fern, but the descendant of an ancient group of fern allies, which dominated the Earth during the Carboniferous era. They are of great evolutionary interest today, when they consist of about 100 generally insignificant species around the world. Coral Fern is difficult to transplant but easy to maintain once it is growing. The fronds have been used to repel cockroaches from houses.

297 Selaginella (Primitive)

Selaginella longipinna is an attractive low growing fern-like plant of moist coastal Queensland. Like the Lycopodiums, above, the Selaginella family is a descendant of ancient fern-like plants which were once much more common than they are today. They are known from many fossils, especially of the Carbonifereous era, when they and other plants formed the basis for the world's largest coal deposits. This Selaginalla, one of over 600 species worldwide, has prostrate creeping branches, resembling true fronds, with 3-4mm leaves in two layers, held close to the stems. The spores are held in strobili, about 10mm long, rising from the branch tips.

298 Fern (Dicranopteris)

Dicranopteris linearis is a hardy scrambling fern commonly found in full sun in road cuttings. The fronds fork in pairs, then fork again. Stems can reach several metres in length, and can form dense masses. Despite this, the plant resents disturbance, and requires constant moisture around the roots. The fronds can be up to 2 metres tall, with leaflets at right angles to the stems, the leaflets whitish underneath. The sori containing the spores are about 1mm across, on a vein, and made up of from 8 to 15 sporangia. This is a widespread species with many forms, found from Cape York to Sydney, also in the NT and throughout the tropics.

299 Gristle Fern

Blechnum cartilagineum is one of a group of 18 species commonly called Water Ferns, which are widespread in Eastern Australia. These are tough, hardy ferns, yet can be found in rainforest in North Queensland. The rhizome or stem of the Gristle Fern is short and thick and covered with black scales. The fronds (>1.5m) grow upright, and are very broad at the base. The leaflets are wider closer to the mid rib. Young fronds are commonly pink, with older fronds a light green, though darker in shaded areas. These ferns can often be found in open gullies or on hillsides. Gristle Fern occurs from Cape York to Tasmania and also in the Philippines. The sori are in continuous rows on each side of the midrib. The fronds with sori may have narrow leaflets.

300 Fern (Dictymia)

Dictymia brownii is found growing in trees or on rocks in rainforest, where the long narrow fronds with prominent rows of sori make this a distinctive fern. The stem or rhizome is long-creeping, and covered with dark scales. The leaves stand stiffly erect, with a prominent midrib. The sori containing the spores are large, oval patches spread on either side of the midrib. The leaves are usually dark green, and without any branching. This is the only Australian representative of a small genus with 4 species, and it occurs from the Atherton Tableland to southern NSW. It is easy to grow, hardy, and is commonly cultivated in a basket.

VINES

301 Slender Cucumber

Zehneria cunninghamii is a slender vine which climbs with tendrils, and produces bright red fruit. It is found along rainforest margins but will grow in open forest. The leaves are broad and triangular, with a toothed margin, with both surfaces usually sandpapery. Flowers may be solitary or in groups. The fruits contain from 4 to 20 white or buff seeds, and may be a pale yellow rather than red. They are eaten by Brown Cuckoo Doves and Lewin's Honeyeaters. Slender Cucumber occurs from the Windsor Tableland west of Mossman to near Sydney in NSW and in the NT and WA. Aboriginal people used this plant as a medicine and for dressings.

Vine >2m   Lf 25-130mm   Fl Feb-Nov 7-8mm   Fr Mar-Nov 6-12mm

302 Coarse Climbing Fern (Lygodium)

Lygodium reticulatum (Above & Below) has tough twining stems that allow it to climb over other vegetation. Lygodiums favour regenerating rainforest, or rainforest margins, and can climb over 25 metres into the trees. There are many variants, making identification difficult. The sporangia grow on the edges of the leaves, like a frill. This species grows in northeast Queensland and into SE Asia. It produces antheridiogens and was used as a herbal remedy for urinary complaints.

303 Small Leaved Fire Vine

Tetracera nordtiana is a vine of the rainforest and rainforest edges. The stems are covered with fine stiff hairs (Left), which allow your hand to slide down the vine, but which grab and 'burn' if you pull against the vine. The leaves are rather distinctive, with deeply marked veins and often serrated edges. Young vines may look like a tree seedling. The flowers are white or cream, and fragrant. The fruit are three horned capsules (Right) which split to reveal a single black seed surrounded by a bright red fleshy aril. Bright fruits are usually bird attractors, and these are eaten by Eclectus Parrots and are a favourite of the Metallic Starlings, swift-flying glossy black birds which live in communal nests.

This is a common vine in the Kuranda area. It occurs from Cape York to near Ingham. It is also found in Malaysia.

Lf 50-100mm   Fl Oct-Mar 6-10mm   Fr Dec-May 5-10mm

304 Common Pepper

Piper caninum is a close relative of the vine which is the source of Pepper, hence the name. It is a root climber and is usually found closely adhering to tree trunks (Left). The pungent leaves are shiny on the upper surface, with a few hairs beneath. The fruits are bunches of small orange berries, growing on a spike opposite a leaf on the vine. The fruit smells peppery if cut and is eaten by Figbirds. The bark and leaves of this vine have produced a variety of chemicals with potential medicinal use. Research at Paluma in North Queensland found a bark extract with strong anti-bacterial activity and an alkaloid extracted from the plant has been found to cause DNA damage. Another chemical has been shown to reduce hypertension in rats. It may seem strange that so many Australian plants have potential medicinal uses, but it is now recognised that the North Queensland rainforest constitutes a remnant of very early rainforest development on Earth, and is a natural repository of many potentially valuable chemicals. More than half the plants tested at Paluma contained chemicals of interest.

Lf 90-200mm   Fl Nov-Jun   Fr Apr -Jan 6-15mm

305 Variegated Grape

Cissus repens is glossy leaved vine which has smooth greeen rounded stems, and is quite closely related to the Wild Grape (see no 66). The glossy leaves are almost heart shaped, held on longish leaf stalks, and have tiny teeth along the margins, with a hair like bristle at the tip of each serration. New growth can be red or purple. The flowers are cream or yellowish green, sometimes tinged with red. The fruits are bunches of brown or black berries about 10mm in diameter. The vine climbs with unbranched tendrils which attach opposite a leaf.

The Variegated Grape occurs from Cape York to the Rockhampton area, growing in rainforest and vine thickets. It also occurs in the NT and through SE Asia to India and China. Although Aboriginal people ate the fruit, it is reputed to burn the tongue and throat. The roots and leaves were used in Chinese medicine. A closely related species, or possibly sub-species, has become a weed in Hawaii.

Lf 70-170mm   Fl Oct-Mar   Fr Dec-Jul 7-12mm

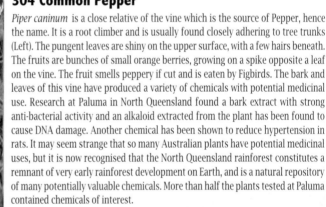

306 Smilax

Smilax blumei is one of six species of Smilax found in North Queensland, most of them as vines with spiny stems. It is shown here (Right) with a flush of bright pink new growth. It is a tendril and hook climber with pairs of tendrils arising from each side of the leaf stalk and hooks along the tough stems. The leaves are a curious rounded shape with a small spike at the apex and are three or five veined. This vine was growing on the edge of rainforest at Kuranda.

Smilax grows in rainforest from Cape York to Cardwell, mostly at lower elevations. It is also found in PNG, Malaysia, and into SE Asia. In Thailand an alcoholic extract is made from the root of this vine and a drink made from it is used as a tonic.

Lf 80-250mm Fl not known in Australia Fr Feb-Mar 6-12mm

307 Austral Sarsaparilla

Smilax australis is another widespread rainforest vine, the leaves more pointed than the Smilax above, though with similar tendrils and hooks along the stems. The colour is due to the new growth.

The leaves are 5-7 veined, though with three dominant veins. White, cream or pink flowers are followed throughout the year by green turning to black fruit with longish stalks containing 1 to 3 red-brown seeds.

This vine occurs across north Australia and as far south as Vic. It attracts birds and butterflies and the leaves have been used as a tonic.

Lf 50-150mm Fl Dec-Aug 5-7mm Fr any month 6-10mm

308 Christmas Vine (Weed)

Turbina corymbosa is an introduced vine which has become especially noticeable along river banks, where the white flowers festoon the vines from May to October. The ropy strands of spaghetti like stems, covered with a pale bark, are readily identified. The leaves are heartshaped and shiny, on long leaf stalks. The flowers are greenish-cream or white, with yellow or brown markings in the throat. The fruits are brown capsules containing a brown hairy seed. The Aztecs called the vine 'Coaxihuitl' and the seeds 'Ololiuqui'. These were used for religious divination and for medicinal purposes, including use as a painkiller.

Christmas Vine can be seen along the Barron River from Mareeba to Kuranda, where it is already choking large trees with its aggressive growth. It is a native of Central America, spread as a garden plant.

Lf 30-140mm Fl May-Oct 20-30mm Fr Jun-Nov 9x5mm

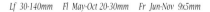

123

Rainforest - Vines

309 Climbing Guinea Flower

Hibbertia scandens is a twiner or scrambler which is most likely to be found on the margins of rainforest. The five petalled, bright yellow flowers are carried above the leaves, and are quite striking, though with an unpleasant scent (some say like almonds). They occur at any time of year. The leaves are dark green on top and

often covered with silvery hairs underneath. The fruits appear as three or four reddish globes held below the brown case of sepals left when the flower petals have fallen. The fruits are eaten by Pigeons and Victoria's Riflebirds. The plant is found from SE NSW (where it grows on beaches) to the Coen area in Cape York. It is also known as **Snake Vine**, and is one of 150 mainly Australian species in this family.

Lf 30-110mm Fl any time 50-70mm Fr Jan-Apr

310 Lacewing Vine (Butterfly Plant)

Adenia heterophylla produces vivid red fruits from Jan to Aug, and is the only Australian Adenia. It is a relative of the Passion fruit, with more or less heart shaped leaves, and tendrils which allow it to grow up to 30 metres into the rainforest canopy. The leaves have two raised glands at the junction to the longish leaf stalk. The small flowers with five petals are cream or pale yellow. The fruits which follow are brightly coloured capsules containing numerous seeds.

The common name Lacewing Vine refers to the fact that this is the host plant for the attractive Red Lacewing butterfly, as well as two other butterfly species, including the Cruiser. It grows between Cape York and Mackay at lower altitudes, and can be seen on the Kuranda Range Road near the big bend. It is also native to the NT, WA and SE Asia.

Lf 40-250mm Fl Oct-Nov >5mm Fr Jan-Aug 40-130mm

311 Pumpkin Vine

Stephania sp (Bamaga) grows from Cape York to south of Cairns. The whitish leaves (Right) are heart shaped with the stalk attached to the middle of the leaf. The most interesting feature of this vine is the very large tuber which forms on the surface of the soil (Below). This one weighs about 15 kg and is about 20 years old.

The soft trailing vine only bears leaves for part of the year. Both sides are pale and commonly smooth, with longish leaf stalks. The tiny orange flowers are followed by bunches of small red fruit. This is one of three Stephania species in Far North Queensland and is not found elsewhere. It is an interesting oddity.

Lf 55-170mm Fl Nov-Dec Fr Jan 8mm

312 Native Dutchman's Pipe (Butterfly Plant)

Aristolochia acuminata is a native vine that is the host for the Cairns Birdwing butterfly, Australia's largest butterfly. The caterpillars (Below, Left) often defoliate the whole plant, before pupating to emerge as the vivid green males or large black females so admired around

Cairns. Unfortunately, there is an introduced Dutchman's Pipe from Indonesia which is poisonous to these butterflies and which is still sold to unsuspecting gardeners who think they are helping the butterflies by planting it. Aristolochia is a twining vine which can grow quite large on trees or a trellis. The leaves (Right) vary from 100 to 300mm in length. The flowers (Top, Left) are a purplish brown colour, with a very distinctive shape. The fruit is a pod, roughly spherical with six segments each ending in a 30mm twisted tail. The numerous seeds have small wings. This vine grows between Cape York and Proserpine and across northern Australia and into SE Asia.

Lf 100-300mm   Fl Oct-Jun 60mm   Fr any month 35-62mm

313 Wild Raspberry (Giant Bramble) (Weed)

Rubus alceifolius is one of the four species of *Rubus*, thorny Raspberry vines, found mainly along the edges of rainforest in North Queensland. This is an introduced species from China. Although the leaf is a little similar, this plant should not be confused with the much more dangerous Stinging Tree (see no 1) which is a shrub or tree and not a vine, with a serrated edge to its leaf. The leaves can be 200mm across, with 5-7 shallow lobes, and carry thorns on the veins, as well as the thorns on the plant's stems. Like the true Raspberry, the fruits are red and follow white flowers. The canes grow up to 5 metres long and are tough and thorny; an impassable barrier to walkers.

Wild Raspberry is common across SE Asia, extending into China (where there are 100 *Rubus* species) and Taiwan. It had medicinal and culinary uses in Thailand and reputedly makes an acceptable jam. It is a noxious weed in Queensland, where it occurs from the Daintree River to south of Mackay and is invasive around Babinda.

Lf 50-200mm   Fl any month 14-20mm   Fr Feb-Aug 15-25mm

314 Rose Leaf Bramble

Rubus queenslandicus is a thorny climber or shrub bearing white flowers and elongated raspberry fruit.

The vine grows to 1.5 metres, with the stems covered in thorns up to 3mm long. The compound leaves are composed of 3-9 leaflets which are prominently toothed, and extend to a fine point. There may be hairs on both surfaces, and possibly thorns on the midrib of the underside of the leaf. The flowers have 5 white petals and are followed by red berries which are reported to be rather dry in texture.

Rose Leaf Bramble occurs from the Windsor Tableland inland from Mossman to near Ingham, mostly at higher altitudes. The fruits are eaten by many species of birds.

Lf 25-90mm   Fl May-Nov 18-22mm   Fr Jun-Feb 8-30mm

315 Native Monstera

Epipremnum pinnatum is a large root climber that closely resembles the Monstera vine that provides an edible fruit. (For those not familiar with it, the flavour is of fruit salad). This Native Monstera shares the very large deeply segmented leaves of its cultivated cousin. It grows roots along the stem, with which it adheres to tree trunks. The green, cream or yellow flowers are minute and clustered on a spike which is surrounded by a most ornamental petal like white or cream spathe. The green fruit is made of many segments that fall off as they ripen. The flesh is orange with numerous strongly curved seeds.

Native Monstera is found along the length of the Queensland coast, as well as in PNG and the Pacific Islands and into SE Asia, where it was used "to blacken the teeth". It is believed to be the same species as the type 'Aureum' with white and yellow leaves that remain unlobed. The sap can be an irritant and the plant is quite poisonous, containing calcium oxalate.

Lf 270-800mm   Fl Aug-Dec on spike >200mm   Fr Nov-Feb 270-550mm

316 Common Hoya

Hoya australis is a common vine with fleshy leaves, a root climber that can grow over rocks or trees. The simple leaves grow in pairs along the vine, each ending in a small spike at the tip. The vine exudes a milky poisonous sap if broken, and produces white or cream 5 petalled flowers. The flowers are fragrant, and have a red base. The fruits are capsules that open along one side with numerous cream seeds.

Common Hoya is found from Cape York to northern NSW, growing in rainforest or open forest. It also occurs in the NT and in WA, and through PNG into Melanesia. Hoyas have been grown by enthusiasts for many years (the original specimen was described in 1830) and numerous varieties now exist. They are easy to grow, but need good drainage. They will grow well in very poor soil and the better blooming varieties will produce clusters of up to 40 waxy flowers during the warmer months. Another common name for the Common Hoya is the **Waxflower**.

Lf 25-150mm   Fl Mar-Oct 10-25mm   Fr Jun-Feb 70-180mm

317 Brazilian Nightshade (Weed)

Solanum seaforthianum is a vine of the rainforest and rainforest edges. It is an introduced weed from the West Indies and produces attractive mauve, purple or violet-blue flowers with yellow stamens from Dec to Aug, followed by bright red berries about 10mm across. The photographs show the vine with immature fruit and (Below) a closer view of the flowers. It is related to the Solanums described earlier and later (see nos 142-144, 336-337).

In Australia Brazilian Nightshade is found from near Coen in Cape York, to Sydney and inland as far as the Brigalow belt of south-central Queensland. Brazilian Nightshade is spread by birds. Regent and Satin Bowerbirds, Superb Fruitdoves, Brown Cuckoo-doves, Varied Trillers, Lewin's Honeyeaters and Silvereyes all feed on the berries. No wonder that seedlings and vines are common.

Lf 40-160mm   Fl Dec-Aug 20-30mm   Fr Feb-Aug 8-12mm

318 Blood Vine (Butterfly Plant)

Austrosteenisia blackii is a large rainforest vine that can cover trees and produce masses of maroon or pink flowers. The vine can reach lengths of 20 metres and can be 400mm thick. It carries compound leaves alternately along the stem, each leaf composed of 5-11 leaflets on short thickened leaf stalks. The main leaf stalk also has a thickened base. The pea-like flowers hang in clusters from the vine. Thin golden-brown seed pods contain between 1 and 8 green or brown seeds.

Blood Vine grows between Cooktown and the Hunter River in NSW. It is common along rivers and rainforest edges.

The Orange Aeroplane butterfly uses Blood Vine as a host plant and the pupae can be found supported by a thread on the vine.

Lf 14-114mm   Fl Sep-Dec 7-10mm   Fr Oct-Jun 35-100mm

319 Austrobaileya (Primitive)

Austrobaileya scandens is a rainforest vine that is actually a 'green dinosaur', the sole representative of one of only 19 families of primitive flowering plants known worldwide. Its pollen resembles some of the oldest pollen known from fossils. The large vine has whitish stems bearing opposed simple leaves with whitish undersides. The unusual flowers, with green tepals and purple dotted stamens, have an unpleasant smell. The orange fruits can be found at any time, and contain two rows of seeds. The stems are attached at an unusual angle. This vine occurs in a small area from Mt Spurgeon to Ravenshoe. Much scientific study has been carried out on this very unusual plant.

Lf 40-200mm   Fl Sep-Oct 50-60mm   Fr any month 38-70mm

320 Pothos (Candle Vine)

Pothos longipes is a climbing plant with roots along the stem which it attaches to tree trunks or rocks. The leaves look like small candles, as the leaf stalk is as wide as the leaf proper, and the leaf is flame shaped. The leaf is simple, and the leaf stalk (10-120mm) is often longer than the leaf. Minute yellow flowers form on a spike about 60mm long. The fruits are bright to dark red berries (8-24mm) each containing 1-3 seeds. Young plants grow zig zag stems. It is believed that the flattened leaf stalks act as extra leaf area in the low light where this vine grows. The dark green of the leaves also absorbs more of the scattered light. Pothos occurs from near Coen to Kendall in NE NSW. This is one of two Australian species.

Lf >15-150mm   Fl Apr&Sep-Dec   Fr Oct-Apr

321 Glory Vine (October Glory)

Faradaya splendida is a large leafed vigorous climber capable of covering the largest rainforest tree. It is the only representative of its family in Australia. The leaves can be huge, and it bears large white fragrant flowers (Left), from Jul to Nov. These are followed with large fleshy fruits (>60mm) which smell of bleach and turn yel-

low when squashed. The white or cream fruit are eaten by Cassowaries, Musky Rat Kangaroos, Spectacled Flying Foxes and Giant White-tailed Rats. The woody seed is itself quite large, and wrinkled like a peach. Aboriginal people used the bark as a fish poison and its flowering indicated that Scrub Turkey eggs were ready to take. Glory Vine is found from Iron Range to Ingham and also in PNG.

Lf 90-390mm Fl Jul-Nov 35-60mm Fr Aug-Apr

322 Misty Bells

Agapetes meiniana (syn. *Paphia meiniana*) is a shrub or vine of mountaintops, where the bright pink or red waxy tubular flowers are commonly found in the wind-swept vegetation. It is related to the Rhododendron which is a rare plant of high places. The Misty Bells plant is an epiphyte, growing on other plants, or lithophyte, growing on rocks. The leaves are simple, and the undersides are dotted with brown glands. The flower is composed of five fused petals. The fruits are purple to black berries containing numerous white or brown tiny seeds. Misty Bells is the only Australian representative of the Agapetes genus, which belongs to the Heather family. It occurs from Mt Finnigan near Cooktown to Mt Bartle Frere, always at high altitude. New growth is an attractive pink colour, and the leaves are glossy. Although considered a rare plant, this recent arrival (>1.6m years ago) from Asia is available as a garden plant which is easy to grow from cuttings.

Lf 30-115mm   Fl Mar-Oct 25-35mm   Fr Jan-May 10-11mm

323 Climbing Bamboo

Bambusa moreheadiana is one of only two bamboos native to the Wet Tropics. It is a climber and not a typical clumping or running bamboo.

Climbing Bamboo scrambles to great heights (>70m) over other vegetation. It grows in wet areas which support a humid and dense rainforest, for example near Innisfail and near Cape Tribulation. The leaves form untidy tufts which spill down from the thin stems. According to one report, the flower has never been observed, and it is assumed that flowering and fruiting is very rare. Some bamboos flower and fruit prolifically in unison, but at long intervals, possibly more than 100 years, after which the plants all die. Typically the number of years between flowerings is a prime number. Such rare events reduce the likelihood of potential seed-eaters preparing for the feast, and the sheer weight of seed ensures plenty are able to germinate. Kew Gardens refers to fertile material from this bamboo so more research is needed on this issue.

324 Carronia

Carronia protensa (Left) is a twining vine which grows grape like bunches of brightly coloured fruit. Those photographed are a dusky pink, but they can be yellow, orange or red. The vine is a twiner, with separate male and female plants. The leaves are an unusual oval shape (See the dark leaf at the top of the photo) on stalks that can be very long, with a swelling where it joins the leaf. Small fragrant green or yellow flowers are followed by the fruits. There are two species of Carronia vine in Australia's rainforests and only four in the world. This species is found only between the Iron Range and Tully, usually at lower altitudes. The photograph comes from near Daintree Villlage.

Lf 65-250mm Fl Oct-Jan Fr Feb-May 15-20mm

325 Vandasina (Butterfly)

Vandasina retusa (Right) is an attractive flowering vine, with distinctive and unusual leaves. It is the only species in its Genus, which belongs to the large Fabaceae family with over 10,000 species worldwide. This is a twining vine, bearing alternate compound leaves (on longish leaf stalks) made up of three heart shaped leaflets. The leaves are shiny, but give the impression that they are the wrong way around on their stalks. The pink or purple pea flowers are held on upright spikes, the standard petals being 7-8mm long, occurring from June to September. The brown or black pods are covered with fine white hairs. They contain 8-10 rather small brown or black seeds. Vandesina retusa occurs from Cape York to Cardwell, near sea level. It is reported to grow near the tip of Cape York, and on dunes near Cape Bedford. It also occurs in PNG and Indonesia. It is one of several host plants to the small orange and black Copper Jewel butterfly. The photographs came from the Rex Range near Mossman.

Lf 30-140mm Fl Jun-Sep 7-8mm Fr Sep-Oct 60-90mm

326 Scrambling Lily

Geitonoplesium cymosum is a wiry stemmed twining vine with delicate leaves and flowers. It, with Wombat Berry (no 160) shares a small family containing just six species worldwide. The leaves are alternated along zig zag stems (Left) with clusters of white or mauve sweetly scented flowers (Right) followed by black berries eaten by Fruit Doves and Bower Birds. Scrambling Lily is found between the Daintree River and Vic, and through PNG and the Pacific to SE Asia. An attractive garden plant, the young shoots are reputed to taste like asparagus.

Lf 20-130mm Fl Sep-May Fr Nov-Jul 7-20mm

327 Chain Fruit

Alyxia ruscifolia is a small shrub with prickly leaves and interesting orange fruit, which is common along rainforest margins near Kuranda. The small leaves may be toothed or smooth edged, but end in a spiny tip. They are carried in whorls of from 3 to 6 leaves. The shrub can grow to 5 metres, and carries small orange fruit, often found in chains of 2 or 3, like beads on a necklace. The flowers are usually white, sometimes cream or yellow, fragrant, and occurring throughout the year. It is one of eight Australian species, and is found from near Wollongong in NSW to the Windsor Tableland, and also in the NT and on Lord Howe Island.

Ht >5m   Lf 15-65mm   Fl any month 3-6mm   Fr Jun-May 6-20mm

328 Hairy Red Pittosporum

Pittosporum rubiginosum is a shrub, growing to 2 metres, with large hairy dark leaves which may grow in whorls. The underside of the leaves, and the leaf stalks, may be purple. All six species of Pittosporum found in the rainforest have orange seed capsules which open to reveal a mass of red seeds, often sticky. The flowers, white, cream or yellow, are borne from Apr to Oct, with fruit all year. Hairy Red Pittosporum grows between Cape York and Proserpine, and the fruit are eaten by Cassowaries, Bush Rats, and Giant White-tailed Rats. This plant has been introduced to tropical gardens with success.

Ht >2m   Lf 40-300mm   Fl Apr-Oct 14-16mm   Fr any month 13-23mm

329 Bandicoot Berry

Leea indica is a shrub with large open compound leaves growing from prominently jointed stems, and with prominent flowers and berrries carried in a head above the leaves. The plant grows in rainforest, and the leaves are usually tripinnate, meaning leaflets are attached to branching stems which are themselves branching. The whole branch-like leaf can be a metre long. Small cream, orange, pink or red flowers are followed by red, purple or black berries that are eaten by Wompoo Fruit-doves. Bandicoot Berry occurs from Cape York to Mackay and also in the NT, SE Asia and India. The juice was used to heal bone fractures and modern research confirms it contains a useful free radical scavenger (like Vitamin C).

Ht >4m   Lf 60-240mm   Fl Sep-Mar Fr Mar-Dec 8-11mm

330 Blue Rubi

Lasianthus strigosus is a rainforest shrub with layered open branches bearing dark blue fruit in season. The plant carries simple leaves in pairs along soft stems, the leaf blades smooth on top, but very hairy underneath. The leaf stalks are quite short. The hairy flowers, about 10mm across, are white and composed of four or five petals. The fruits are the most striking feature of this plant. They are deep blue and form bunches at each node where the leaves are attached. They have a taffeta like appearance due to a covering of very short hairs. The fruits smell unpleasant when cut and contain four cream to brown seeds. Blue Rubi belongs to a widespread tropical family with only two Australian species. It occurs from just south of Cape York to near Cardwell, mostly at low altitude. It is also found in PNG and into Asia. This is one of about 80 plants, mostly rather primitive, that have been found to accumulate aluminium. The Blue Rubi may make a desirable garden plant though it is probably short lived.

Ht >3m   Lf 140-200mm   Fl Apr-Feb 10mm   Fr Feb-Dec 10-16mm

331 Oak (Daintree Pine) (Primitive Plant)

Gymnostoma australianum is one of the rarest plants in North Queensland and one you are unlikely to see in the wild. However, it is one of a select group of truly ancient plants, and has survived at 5 sites on two creeks near Cape Tribulation; Noah Creek to the east of Thornton Peak, and Roaring Meg to the west. Now available from nurseries it can be seen in the Cairns Botanic Gardens. The female flow-

ers (Left) are small, with a red or pink style, while the fruits are Casuarina like cones. This plant is in the same family as the Casuarinas (see no 51) but is an extremely primitive member of it, able to be traced back to 50 million year old fossils. The attractive pine like conical shape ensures the future for this survivor. It is in demand as a Christmas tree, and thrives in a pot.

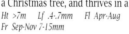

Ht >7m   Lf .4-.7mm   Fl Apr-Aug
Fr Sep-Nov 7-15mm

332 Gardenia (Primitive Plant)

Gardenia actinocarpa is another extremely rare plant, but one you may encounter if you visit the Marrdja boardwalk at Noah Creek on the way to Cape Tribulation.

This attractive white flowering Gardenia is perhaps the ancestor of all modern Gardenias. The shrub carries elongated multiveined leaves in pairs on short stems, in almost whorled arrangements on the branches. The leaves may be smooth or sandpapery, and the white or cream fragrant flowers precede ribbed green or yellow fruits containing several seeds.

This rare Gardenia occurs only near sea level on Noah and Oliver Creeks. It is known to set few fruit, so is listed as endangered.

Ht >5m   Lf 70-270mm   Fl Aug-Feb 60mm   Fr Sep-Jan 28-46mm

333 Wenlock Gardenia

Larsenaikia ochreata is a shrub or tree with untidy leaves and attractive white flowers throughout the year. The tree can reach 20m in height, losing its leaves for a period, and has separate male and female plants. The leaves are simple, with 12-18 pairs of lateral veins and a hairy surface. Flowers have 5 or 6 petals which can

be white, cream or yellow. The yellowish green fruit are finely hairy, and have a prominent tubular extension on the end. Wenlock Gardenia is found between Cape York and Rockhampton in rainforest or open forest. As the flowers are showy and fragrant, and the plant can withstand drought, it has potential for use in horticulture.

Ht >20m   Lf 50-120mm   Fl any month
34-80mm   Fr Mar-Dec 22-50mm

334 Bolwarra (Primitive Plant)

Eupomatia laurina is a shrub or small tree which grows distinctive dry berries containing numerous seeds. All three species of Eupomatia occur in Australia, this one also is found in PNG. The plant carries simple leaves which are aromatic when crushed. The flowers have neither petals nor sepals, but lots of glossy white fragrant stamens. The fruits are filled with cream or brown seeds in a yellowish flesh. It occurs from Cooktown to Victoria. The fruits resemble guavas, and jellies and jams are made from them. **Native Guava** is another common name. Aboriginal people made spears from the wood and string from the inner bark. This primitive plant from an ancient family contains medicinal and anti fungal compounds.

Ht >10m Lf 50-200mm Fl Oct-Nov 20-25mm Fr Jan-Jul >45mm

335 Sandfly Bush

Zieria smithii is a shrub of high rainforest or wet open forest areas with dark green leaves and contrasting white flowers. The shrub carries twigs that may be smooth or hairy. The leaves are compound, with usually three small leaflets attached to a longish leaf stalk. The leaves, which occur in opposed pairs, are aromatic and dotted with tiny black glands. Small white, cream or pink flowers occur in Mar-Apr and Jul-Sep, followed by clusters of small green, pink, red or brown capsules containing one or two brown or black seeds. Sandfly Bush is found from the Windsor Tableland to Tasmania, and a rare form in NSW is listed as endangered. The leaves contain some unpleasant smelling oils that act as an insect repellant, and the plant produces a yellow dye. It has been used as a garden plant, and is reputed to relieve headaches.

Ht >2m   Lf 10-45mm   Fl Mar-Apr&Jul-Sep   Fr Apr-Sep 3mm

HERBS etc

336 Devil's Apple (Weed)

Solanum capsicoides is a poisonous weed of rainforest edges and disturbed ground. It is a native of Brazil that is now found from Cairns to Sydney. The stems and lobed leaves bear thin straight spines up to 12mm long. The flowers are white with bright yellow stamens. The bright red ornamental fruits, which have led to the spread of this plant as a garden plant, are borne throughout the year. Devil's Apple has become an invasive weed in some Pacific islands. The plant in the photograph was growing near Kuranda on the edge of rainforest.

Ht >2m   Lf 30-180mm   Fl Aug-Oct&Jan-Mar 20-30mmm   Fr Oct-Jun 20-35mm

337 Nightshade

Solanum viridifolium is a shrub bearing bright red berries on long stems. This bush can grow to a small tree with a few spines on the stems. The leaves may be hairy when young, generally shiny when mature. The flowers occur at any time, and vary from white to cream, pink, purple or blue. The red berries contain numerous small seeds, and are eaten by pigeons. Nightshade is also known as **Boolally**, and is found from Cape York to Rockhampton, growing at a range of altitudes. The fruits are not edible and may be toxic. All native fruits should be treated with great caution as many are poisonous, and a misidentification could cost you your life.

Ht >7m   Lf 30-190mm   Fl any month 15-18mm Fr any month 7-10mm

338 Native Banana

Musa banksii looks very similar to the domestic banana, and grows a bunch of rather similar fruit, which are, however, full of seeds and almost inedible. The 'tree', which is really a giant herb, can grow to 6 metres in height. The chocolate brown trunk is quite soft, made up of the folded stems of the leaves, and can be easily cut through with one hit of a strong knife. The white, cream or yellow flower is followed by the bunch of bananas, which slowly ripen, and when ripe the tree dies.

Bunches tend to grow horizontally, with the fruit strongly inclined to grow vertically, but heavier bunches hang downwards. New plants can grow from suckers which arise at the base of the main plant (Above, Right), often forming a clump. The Native Banana is found from Iron Range in Cape York to near Townsville. It also grows in PNG and Samoa. Aboriginal people north of Cairns ate the cooked inner trunk, cut just as the flower emerged, as well as the fruit when fully ripe.

Ht >6m   Lf 1.2-2.3m   Fl Aug-Jun 27-45mm   Fr Oct-Jul 80-140mm

339 Coral Berry (Weed)

Ardisia crenata is a native of Asia now found throughout coastal Queensland. This shrub grows to 2 metres, but is commonly seen flowering and fruiting at a much smaller size. The leaves have rounded teeth (the meaning of 'crenata') and are shiny, with veins around the margins somewhat hidden by the way the edges fold inwards. The attractive white or cream flowers are followed by bunches of bright red berries.

Coral Berry is found from Japan through China into northern India. It is considered an invasive weed in Australia and Florida, with the seeds spread by birds. This plant can be seen on the outskirts of Kuranda, growing in moist forest. It contains saponins and the root is used to stimulate blood circulation. It has been spread mainly as a garden plant.

Ht >2m   Lf 50-120mm   Fl Nov-May 8-10mm   Fr Feb-Aug 5-10mm

340 Native Coleus

This *Plectranthus* species grows in shade on the margins of rainforest. It is one of 12 species which are fairly similar, having soft hairy leaves with serrated margins, and spikes of purple, blue or white flowers (Left). Some have strongly scented foliage, but the odour, which may resemble 'five spice', does not persist in cooking. The plant pictured is possibly *Plectranthus graveolens*, which has blue flowers, and is found between Iron Range and Northern NSW. It has a large number of teeth on each side of the leaf, which distinguishes it from many of the other species. It would be necessary to look for glands on the leaves and to smell the crushed leaves to be more certain of the identity of this species, which was photographed at the Clohesy River boardwalk.

Ht >2m Lf 25-105mm Fl Jan-Oct 8-9mm Fr Jul-Jan 1mm

341 Stinking Cockspur Flower

Plectranthus foetidus is another species of Plectranthus, found on rainforest margins, with hairy leaves that are unpleasantly scented if crushed. The plant grows simple leaves with from 9-34 teeth per side, hairy on both sides, and the underside dotted with tiny yellow to orange glands. The leaf stalks are variable in length. The flowers are in heads, with the fused petals white, pink, purple or blue. The small brown or black fruits are enclosed in a densely hairy calyx, and ripen in November. The name Stinking Cockspur Flower has been given to this plant due to the mildly nauseaous smell of the flowers. Many of the Plectranthus family produce compounds poisonous to mites. This plant occurs between Cooktown and the Tully Falls.

*Ht >2m   Lf 20-100mm   Fl Jul-Nov 7-11mm
Fr Nov 3-5mm*

342 Wandering Jew

Commelina ensifolia is also known as **Scurvy Weed**. It is a soft creeping plant that favours damp areas, and partial shade, but will grow in full sun. The flowers are commonly blue (Left & Right), but can be white. The fruits are 2 or 3 valved brown capsules up to 6mm long. Leaves are lancelike and the leafstalk sheathes the soft stems.

Wandering Jew is widely spread down the Eastern coast of Australia, from Cape York to central NSW, and is found in rainforest and along rainforest margins near Cairns. However it grows in dryer inland areas as well, and commonly occurs after good rains even in quite arid areas. It is also found in the NT, in WA and SA, and north through PNG into Melanesia and Asia.

Lf 20-120mm   Fl Oct-Jun 8-26mm   Fr Jan-Jun 6mm

343 Pollia

Pollia macrophylla is a close relative of Wandering Jew (Above), and is sometimes known by that name also. It is a larger plant, common along trails in rainforest, where it can grow to 2 metres tall. The similar *Pollia crispata* grows to 1 metre. The shiny leaves of this Pollia are lance shaped, and fleshy, and the leaf stalks sheathe the stem. The flowers are commonly white, blue, or purple from Oct to Jan. They grow on a spike that is 75-100mm long, while the spike of *Pollia crispata* is only 50mm long. The purplish or grey fruits contain 10-18 small seeds.

Pollia occurs between Iron Range in Cape York and northern NSW. A smaller species is found on the Atherton Tablelands. Pollia grows on the trail at the foot of Kahlpahlim Rock. Older leaves can be eaten as a spinach, but growing tips can be bitter.

Ht >2m   Lf 100-240mm   Fl Oct-Jan 6-12mm   Fr Nov-Aug 5-6mm

344 Turkey Berry (Coral Berry) (Weed)

Rivina humilis is an introduced herb or shrub bearing spikes of bright red berries. It comes originally from Central America and is widespread in the Tropics where it has become a weed in many places, including in North Queensland. The shrub is normally low growing (the meaning of 'humilis') with toothed or smooth edged shiny leaves with long leaf stalks. The flowers have four white, green or pink sepals, growing in spikes, followed by small but attractive red or orange berries . The fruits are eaten by the Brown Cuckoo-dove, and the seeds are spread by this and other birds. Turkey Berry is found from Cape York to close to Sydney in NSW. It is commonly found on the edge of rainforest, where it can smother other plants. The berries are toxic to humans but the plant is widely used as an ornamental garden species.

Ht >2m   Lf 40-120mm   Fl Mar-Aug   Fr Apr-Aug 3-4mm

345 Native Ginger

Alpinia caerulea is one of the common rainforest gingers. The fronds of Gingers are easily recognisable, with the large paired leaflets along a slender rather drooping stalk. Native Ginger bears white, cream or pink flowers on a stalk rising above the end of the frond. These are followed by green berries which turn blue as they ripen. Each fruit contains about 30 seeds that are black when ripe. The fronds grow to 4 metres in length, and several may form a clump above an underground rhizome. It is the rhizome which provides the fruit in the related edible Ginger.

Ht >4m Lf 240-550mm Fl Sep-Apr Fr 10-18mm

346 Pleated Ginger

Alpinia arctiflora is another rainforest ginger with similar flowers and fronds to the Native Ginger (Above) but with elongated fruits that turn grey when ripe. The plants grow to 4 metres, with simple leaves either side of the long stems. The underside of the leaves is densely hairy, and feels like down. The ruffled flowers are white, hence the name 'arctiflora'. There is a yellow spot at the base of the main lipped petal known as a labellum. The three valved grey fruit capsule contains numerous black or brown stony seeds, held within a whitish papery aril. These fruits are eaten by Cassowaries.

Pleated Ginger occurs in a small area of North Queensland between Cooktown and Paluma (North of Townsville) at a range of altitudes. It has been used as an ornamental garden plant.

Ht >4m Lf 360-550mm Fl Aug-Apr 24-40mm Fr Feb-Aug 30-85mm

347 Stalkless Ginger

Alpinia modesta is another rainforest ginger which is a smaller plant than the two above. The plant is usually no more than 1 metre tall (rarely to 2m) and can form clumps in rainforest (Below, Right). The stems are commonly reddish black, and the leaves are shiny, often red beneath, and without leaf stalks. The flowers are in a dense head, with the striking lipped petal known as a labellum white or cream with pink to reddish markings and a yellowish centre. The clusters of blue fruit each contain 12-22 brown seeds in a white papery aril.

Stalkless Ginger occurs in a small area of North Queensland from Cape Tribulation to Paluma north of Townsville. The tuber is reputedly edible with a ginger-like taste, and the reddish leaves and compact shape make this a fine garden plant.

Ht >1m Lf 100-320mm Fl Jun&Oct-Jan 5-19mm Fr Feb-Apr 9-15mm

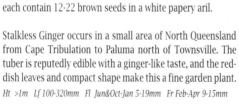

348 Palm Lily

Cordyline cannifolia has broad strap like radiating leaves supported on a thin stem, often growing in clumps. The underside of the leaves is whitish. The red fruit hang from the apex of the plant, which rarely exceeds 2 metres in height. The leaves are paired in a spiral. Clusters of white, pink, cream or mauve flowers are followed by red berries, which are eaten by many birds, and the Fawn-footed Melomys. Palm Lily grows from Cape York to Gladstone and in the NT and PNG. The leaves contain minute needle like crystals (raphides) of calcium oxalate.

Ht >2m   Lf 180-500mm   Fl Apr-Nov
Fr Jan-Jul 10-14mm

349 Giant Palm Lily (Slender Palm Lily)

Cordyline manners-suttoniae is closely related to the Palm Lily (Above) but lacks the white underside to the leaves, and can grow to 5 metres. The leaves are shiny, in whorled pairs, but old leaves turn yellow on the edges. The white or cream flowers are followed by yellow to red fruits (Right) which hang from the apex of the plant in an attractive bunch. Figbirds eat these fruits.

The Giant Palm Lily occurs from Iron Range in Cape York to Rockhampton, It can be seen on Mt Whitfield near Cairns. Pacific Islanders call cordylines 'Ti', and New Zealanders know them as Cabbage Trees or Palms. There is a highly prized variegated form. Plants can be grown from tops, stem cuttings, tuber cuttings or seed, taking up to 3 years to flower from seed.

Ht >5m   Lf 350-650mm   Fl Feb-Jul 10mm   Fr Dec-May 8-15mm

350 Red-headed Cottonbush (Weed)

Asclepius curassavica is a poisonous weed from the West Indies which has become naturalised in Australia and which occurs in a wide range of habitats including rainforest. The plant grows to 1.5m in height, and grows opposed lance-like dark green leaves, the leaf stalks bearing glands at their base. The bright orange-red 5petalled flowers grow in a bunch near the top of the plant. The fruits are capsules that split along one side to release several poisonous brown seeds attached to long silky hairs. These are carried by the wind.

Red-headed Cottonbush is commmon in coastal areas of Queensland, and occurs from Coen to Sydney in NSW. It is well known in the US as a butterfly plant, one of the hosts to the Monarch butterfly. In fact it is so attractive it can cause the butterfly to lay its eggs prematurely when grown outside its normal range. It was used in Chinese medicine, and produces asclepin, which has cardiotonic activity.

Ht >1.5m   Lf 60-170mm   Fl Sep-Mar 8-15mm   Fr any month 50-90mm

351 Cunjevoi

Alocasia brisbanensis is a Lily like plant, the only representative of its genus in Australia. It is commonly found in rainforest close to Stinging Tree (See no 1) and its sap is widely believed to ease the sting of the Stinging Tree, though there is little evidence that it works. While it can grow to 2 metres in height, it is usually much less, with big fleshy leaves. The plant illustrated (Right) has both flower and fruit visible. The tiny flowers are clustered on the cream spike to the right of the plant, while the unripe seeds are visible in the sheathed capsules. Eventually the yellow, orange and red berries will be visible on a spike that rises above the peeled back capsule. Many birds, including the Cassowary and the Spotted Catbird, eat the fruit. Cunjevoi grows from Cooktown in North Queensland to Ulladulla in NSW. All parts are poisonous to humans.

Ht >2m Lf 450-700mm Fl Aug-Jan on spike>140mm Fr Oct-Mar 6-11mm

352 Taro

Colocasia esculenta is a lily-like herb commonly found growing in or near water, and with large elephant-ear leaves. The plant roots from the nodes, and develops underground rhizomes which are edible (the meaning of 'esculenta') after cooking or fermenting to remove the irritant crystals of calcium oxalate in leaves and corms. The large simple leaves are whitish underneath, smooth and rather matte textured on top. The leaf stalks (>1m) are smooth and green, purple or red in colour. Tiny fragrant flowers cluster on a yellow to orange spike. The fruits are green berries also on a spike, containing numerous minute seeds. Taro occurs between the Palmer River and northern NSW, in the NT and WA, the Pacific Islands, SE Asia and India. It has been a staple food for millions and produces a readily digested starch and nutritious greens.

Ht >1.5m Lf 90-600mm Fl Jan-Mar&Oct Fr 3-5mm

353 Ivy-leaved Violet

Viola hederacea is a small violet with attractive white to purple flowers above a rosette of fan like leaves. This perennial herb grows simple leaves that are wider than they are long, carried on long leaf stalks from 20 to 120mm long. The sometimes fragrant flower produces a 3 valved capsule (Mar-Jun&Dec) containing white, brown or black seeds. It is found on rainforest margins and in open forest from the Windsor Tableland to Tas and also SA with a possible occurrence in Malaysia. There are about 500 species of violet in the world, with only six native to Australia. Ivy-leaved Violet grows well as a ground cover, forming dense mats in cool moist situations. It is reputed to have medicinal and culinary uses.

Ht >120mm Lf 8-30mm Fl Oct-Jun Fr 4-6mm

354 Christmas Orchid

Calanthe triplicata is a showy white ground orchid that has been eliminated in parts of its range by over collecting. The flowering spike can be over a metre tall and bears numerous white flowers which mark badly if handled, turning grey, indigo or blue from indican, which also occurs in Woad, the English plant dye. There are small pseudo bulbs and generally 3-4 large pleated leaves. While found growing on the ground, this plant will grow in leaf litter on rocks, and is shallow rooted. Christmas Orchid occurs between the Bloomfield River and the Illawarra District in NSW, as well as through SE Asia into India and China. It is the only Calacanthe in Australia, and grows easily with mulch.

Ht >1m+   Lf >900mm   Fl Oct-Jan 30mm

355 Weevil Lily

Molineria capitulata is a lily with striking pleated leaves not unlike a small palm, and with unimpressive small yellow flowers. The plant can grow to 1 metre, with simple alternate leaves radiating from the butt, on stalks up to 700mm long. The cream or yellow flowers are near ground level (Right), and are followed by hairy cream to brown berries containing numerous dark seeds. In Queensland this plant

occurs only from Mossman to Innisfail near sea level, but it is found also in the NT, PNG, and through SE Asia to India. This plant produces unusual leaf movements where a leaf may oscillate from 40-120 times per minute, then stop. It is now thought the plant is able to act as an antenna for weak geomagnetic variations, resulting in the movement.

Ht >1m Lf 600-1500mm Fl Sep-Feb 8-12mm
Fr Aug-Feb 7-16mm

356 Stinking Roger (Weed)

Tagetes minuta is a tall annual weed with an unpleasant smell often found on road sides on the margins of rainforest. The plant favours damp disturbed sites, and grows ribbed stems. The leaves are compound with 3-9 leaflets opposite at the base and alternate near the top of the plant, with saw tooth edges showing dark glands. The small flowers are white with yellow florets in a tube about 10mm long. Stinking Roger occurs between the Windsor Tableland west of Mossman to Bega in NSW. It originated in South America and is now naturalised in Australia. While a weed here, in Argentina and Chile it produces a tea-like, licorice flavoured drink, Chinchilla, which at greater strengths is a medicine for colds and stomach ailments. It produces tagetes oil, used in perfumes and flavouring Cola drinks and icecream. It is also effective against fungi, roundworms and nematodes.

Ht >2m   Lf 10-80mm   Fl Jun 10mm   Fr Jul 5-8mm

357 Resurrection Plant

Borya septentrionalis is a most unusual plant forming tufts or mats over rock, mainly at high altitude. Its other common name of **Porcupine Bush** alerts you to its prickly nature, but it is its ability to change from its vivid orange form (Above) to green after rain that gives it the name above. It is commonly associated with King Orchids (Plant at Left of photo Above - also see no 368) which favour the same exposed locations. It grows white globular flowers on short stalks raised above the surface of the plant. Together with Mountain Couch (Below) it survives on widely scattered survival niches on rocky mountains. This species appears to be endemic to NE Queensland. A very similar related species occurs in southern WA. While it looks like a spiky grass or giant moss, it is actually more closely related to the Lilies. This plant occcurs on Walsh's Pyramid, south of Cairns, as well as on Kahlpahlim Rock.

358 Mountain Couch

Micraira subulifolia forms mats on rock rather like Resurrection Plant (Above), though they are somewhat softer and do not turn bright orange when dry. This unusual grass is found at only a few widely separated sites. It is the host of a rare fungus. The patch in the photograph (Left) is near the Davies Creek Falls, on an area of rock that stays wet from seepage after rain. It is also found on the Pyramid, near Cairns.

There are about 25 Australian plants that have foliage which revives after dehydration. Mountain Couch is found in Far North Qld and also in the Glasshouse Mountains.

359 Settler's Flax (Primitive Plant)

Gymnostachys anceps is a sedge like plant with long thin leaves, bearing flowers and fruits on structures that develop near the leaf tips. The plant (>2m) is an understory plant of rainforest, and is the only species in its genus, endemic to Australia between Cooktown and Milton in NSW. The long, simple leaves (1-2m) can be smooth or toothed, with ridged veins, and teeth on the mid rib near the apex. The flowers (Jan-Nov) are minute and clustered on a spike (20-40mm) near the tip of the leaf. The fruits (Jan-May) are purple or blue berries (13-16mm) containing a single green seed eaten by Satin Bowerbirds. Settler's Flax has interesting roots - young roots are long, white, plump feeder roots that store starch; while older plants develop a short, thick, cylindrical rhizome that stores starch and grows from the top. This plant may be an ancestor to all grasses. Its tough leaves were used as string.

360 Saw Sedge (Sword Grass) (Butterfly Plant)

Gahnia sieberiana is a tall thin leaved sedge with sharp leaf margins that can inflict cuts on unwary walkers. It is common under the Allocasuarina trees (see no 385) found on ridges in, and along the edges of, rainforest. The serrated edged leaves can reach lengths of 4 metres on stems up to 10m long, though 2 metres is

more common. Black flowers are borne in clusters on stems (>3m) in Spring and Summer, and are followed by shiny red-brown seeds. The leaves of Saw Sedge cut due to the silica granules that occur on their surface and edges. Deep cuts are common. Nevertheless this sedge can make an interesting feature plant for landscaping, replacing the introduced Pampas Grass that is becoming a weed in some areas. Saw Sedge occurs from Cape York to Tasmania and into SA. It is the easiest to grow of the 20 Australian species of Gahnia (there are 30 species world wide). It is the host plant for some southern butterflies, including the Sword Grass Brown.

361 Large Seeded Gahnia (Butterfly)

Gahnia aspera is a grassy looking sedge with prickly leaves and prominent seedheads bearing a spiral of reddish seeds. The stems (>1.5m) are solid, with 3 or 4 nodes, and are perennial. The simple leaves (>1m) are minutely toothed and shiny. The fruits are a nut (4-6mm) containing a single cream, brown or black seed. These are eaten by the Pied Currawong.

Large Seeded Gahnia is found from Cape York to Southern NSW, and also in the Pacific Islands and SE Asia.

Aboriginal people ate the leaf buds raw and pounded the nuts to make a flour. While a useful garden plant, this Gahnia is difficult to propogate. Like Saw Sedge (above) the leaves can inflict nasty cuts. This Gahnia is also the host to two butterfly species.

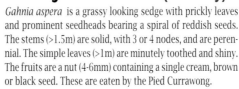

141

362 Slender Climbing Pandan

Freycinetia excelsa is a close relative of Pandanus, but the leaves are smaller and the plant forms a climber with roots appearing along the stems. These vines can climb quite high into the canopy. The leaves can vary greatly in length (150-730mm) and

are toothed along the margins and spiny on the underside. The fruit is similar to the Scrub Breadfruit, but much smaller (>50x25mm) from Dec to Apr, coloured orange when ripe. The five Australian species of Freycinetia are all found in North Queensland, this one extending as far South as northern NSW, and is also in the NT and PNG.

363 Climbing Pandan

Freycinetia scandens is a broad leaved Pandan bearing multiple fruit at the ends of the branches. This climbing vine has roots along the stems with male and female plants. The leaves (90-130mm) surround the stem, with no leaf stalk, and are shiny and smooth though with small teeth at each end of the leaf blade, and sometimes with spines under the mid rib near the apex. Flowers occur in clusters of up to 3 spikes at the ends of branches, with white or green bracts on male flowers; red on female. The fruits (Oct-Apr) are composed of red segments that occur on heads (48-55mm) containing numerous minute seeds. Climbing Pandan occurs from Cooktown to Nambour and is also found in PNG and SE Asia. It is an excellent indoor plant, and is being promoted as bearing edible fruit with the flavour of strawberries. It is pollinated by a fruit sucking moth.

364 Pup Pandan

Pandanus gemmifer can be found in rainforest, but is also found along streams between Coen and Paluma. It is common at Crystal Cascades where it overhangs the stream. The leaves (>2.3m) are without thorns near the base, but have thorns on edges and the midrib further along. The fruits (200-300mm) are bright red (May-Jan) and are made up of many segments, somewhat resembling a pineapple. The stems have short thorns protruding through slits in the bark and prop roots at the base.

Small plants ('pups') form beneath the large rosettes of spiny leaves (Left). These pups can fall to start a new plant. One curious fact about this Pandanus, and some others, is that the spiral direction of the leaves is reversed after each flowering. Aboriginal people used pandanus leaves for weaving.

365 Fungus Root

Balanophora fungosa might look like a fungus and sound like a fungus, but it is actually a flowering plant that is a root parasite. Though not often noticed, it is quite common in rainforest. The leaves, which do not bear chlorophyll, are pink, yellow, orange or brown scales, just visible in the photograph (Right) below the round fruit receptacles. These carry the tiny female flowers, while the white, club-like male flowers form a ring below, visible around the lower left plant. These plants grow to about 80mm in height, often partly hidden by leaf litter. This is the only Australian species.

Fungus Root is found from Iron Range to Gympie in southern Queensland. It occurs in Fiji, SE Asia and India. Many plants do have associations with root fungi, which are often symbiotic, each assisting the other. This plant, though, is a parasite.

366 Rattle Skulls

Dischidia major is a vine with strange inflated leaves or bladders as well as smaller leaves resembling its close relative the Button Orchid (see no 23). Both can be seen in the photograph. The vine clings to trees with roots emerging from the nodes where the leaves are attached. The large inflated leaves (35-90mm) have short leaf stalks, while the smaller flat leaves (15-26mm) have very short leaf stalks and tiny raised glands at the base. Small 5-petalled cream, yellow or orange flowers with dark red tips occur throughout the year. The green or brown fruits are pods (45-80mm) that split along one side to release numerous seeds attached to plumes that allow them to float on the wind. Rattle skulls are related to Hoyas (see no 316) and occur in rainforest, open forest, and in swampy areas from Cape York to Port Douglas. They also occur in PNG and SE Asia. The developing leaf folds in on itself to create a pickle like chamber. This is then inhabited by ants from the genus Philidris, which bring nutrient rich waste into the chamber. The plant then develops roots in the chamber, and ultimately derives 40% of its carbon and 30% of its nitrogen needs from the ants. The ants gain a protected home, and may defend the plant against other insects. Rattle Skulls make interesting pot plants.

367 Zamia Fern

Bowenia spectabilis is an attractive and unusual small cycad with fern like leaves. The plant can reach 2 metres, with 2 or 3 frond like leaves, the leaflets (50-180mm) having smooth edges, though sometimes deeply serrated, and growing from a carrot shaped or branching underground tuber up to100mm thick. Male plants grow narrow green-brown cones (80mm high) which swell and warm (by 4-6°C) while emitting a musty odour that attracts pollinating weevils. The rarer female cones (Left) are barrel shaped (>200mm) and swell for a day or so to receive pollen, then grow for another six months with pink, lilac or blue seeds developing. The male cones disintegrate after heavy rain. Animals such as the Musky Rat-kangaroo spread the seeds. Aboriginal people ate the seeds after much preparation, as they are quite poisonous. Zamia Fern is found in wet forest between Coen and Townsville.

368 King Orchid

Dendrobium speciosum is one of the few orchids that you may encounter in spectacular bloom, mainly on rocky outcrops. Those at right were growing amongst Resurrection Plants at Kahlpahlim Rock, where they bloom usually in Sep to Oct. The flowers (>120/stem) are borne on strong 600mm stems and are white to creamy yellow, with a delicate fragrance. King Orchids were quickly introduced into the gardens of early settlers, where they sometimes grew into huge plants. Their range is from Gippsland (Vic) to near Cooktown. Slow to flower, they are one of the showiest orchids in the world. (See also no 357 for a view of the plant.)

369 Orchid

This small orchid, *Cadetia taylorii* (Left) was growing on lichen covered rock at high altitude. The plant (80-90mm) has a small white flower (>10mm) with a vanilla fragrance duing the day. It is typical of many species that thrive on rocks or trees at these altitudes. Often rocks are carpeted with tiny orchids, whose flowers may be no larger than a match head. While over 120 orchids grow in Cape York, and many are found in rainforest, the reality is that it is rare to see spectacular flowers while walking. If you take time to look, you will find that many rainforest trees do host orchids, and if you are fortunate, you may find some in flower.

Some Other Rainforest Plants in this book.

TREES: Stinging Tree *(Dendrocnide moroides)* #1 p10 **Blue Quandong** *(Eleaocarpis grandis)* #40 p26 **Umbrella Tree** *(Schefflera actinophylla)* #41 p27 **Cadaghi** *(Corymbia torelliana)* #94 p47 **Small-fruited Fig** *(Ficus microcarpa)* #103 p51 **Small-leaved Fig** *(Ficus obliqua)* #104 p51 **Brown Macaranga** *(Macaranga mallotoides)* #106 p52 **Red Kamala** *(Mallotus philippensis)* #108 p52 **White Cedar** *(Melia azedarach)* #116 p56 **Pink Poplar** *(Euroschinus falcata)* #117 p56 **Mango Bark** *(Canarium australasicum)* #118 p56 **Acacia Cedar** *(Paraserianthes toona)* #119 p57 **Glossy Tamarind** *(Guoia acutifolia)* #129 p60 **Harvey's Buttonwood** *(Glochidion harveyanum)* #135 p62 **Brush Cypress Pine** *(Callitris macleayana)* #395 p154 **Flame Tree** *(Brachychiton acerifolius)* #476 p182

VINES: Wait-a-While *(Calamus moti)* #2 p11 (Also *Calamus radicalis* and *Calamus australis* #3 & #4 p11) **Supplejack** *(Flagellaria indica)* #156 p69

OTHER: Scrub Breadfruit *(Pandanus monticola)* #78 p40 **Yellow Pittosporum** *(Pittosporum revolutum)* #413 p160 **Fan Palm** *(Licuala ramsayii)* #62 p35 **Black Palm** *(Normanbya normanbyi)* #63 p35

INLAND OPEN FOREST

West of the narrow belt of rainforest begins the inland open forest that stretches for hundreds of kilometers towards the west coast of Queensland. While it overlaps with the coastal open forest we have already examined, there is sufficient difference to justify a section for itself. In part this is due to drier conditions west of the coastal ranges, and in part it is because there is a different range of plants to the west, adapted to dry conditions for most of the year and resistant to burning. We know from pollen studies that the western edge of the rainforest has moved quite dramatically over a period of tens of thousands of years, reflecting chiefly changes in climate. This dynamic boundary can be very sharply defined. In places you can move from open forest into rainforest with just one or two steps. Fire maintains the boundary.

Many visitors, and indeed many Australians, find the inland bush monotonous. Driving for hundreds of kilometers, there may be little obvious change from hour to hour. It is important to stop and walk if you are really to see this environment and its subtly changing plant life. Davies Creek National Park and Emerald Creek Falls are good areas to explore inland open forest close to Cairns and both are easily accessible. While the open forest can appear hot and dry and somewhat hostile, it actually is easier to make out what is present than in the rainforest, and the seasonal variation, especially after rain, is obvious. Wildflowers can be spectacular in their season, with many blooming during the wet season, rather than in Spring. The open forest has its subtleties and nuances.

370 Leichhardt Tree

Nauclea orientalis is found in rainforest and open forest, often along waterways, where it grows into a quite large tree with buttresses. The blunt ended leaves are very large with strongly marked veins. The flowers, up to 40mm across, are striking

though not often seen, as they last only a few days. The fruit, similar in size and shape, are brown. Leichhardt was a famous explorer who vanished in 1848, having previously explored the Lynd River area of North Queensland.

Ht >30m Lf 70-300mm Fl Sep-Mar Fr Dec-Jul 40-50

371 Brush Box

Lophostemon confertus grows in rainforest and in open forest, especially along creeks. The photographs (Right) show trees at the same location on Davies Creek. The top one is showing stress from drought at the end of November, with the leaves constricted into little bunches at the ends of the branches. Two months later (Below) the leaves have revived after the wet season has begun. Brush Box has rough brown to grey bark at the base, with smooth, pink/orange, flakey bark up higher. New shoots are covered with white hairs. The frilly white flowers (Left) are scented. Brush Box occurs from Cooktown to central NSW and is an invasive weed in Hawaii. It is used as a garden plant in Australia.

Ht >40m   Lf 70-175mm   Fl Aug-May 20-25mm Fr Sep-May 8-10mm

372 Northern Swamp Box

Lophostemon grandiflorus resembles Brush Box (Above) in its leaves and flowers, but has a dark grey or black fibrous bark over the whole trunk and limbs. The tree often occurs along waterways. The simple leaves may be hairy or shiny, and the undersides are whitish. The leaf stalks usually carry white hairs, and may be up to 30mm long. The five petalled fragrant flowers are white or cream with a green centre. The fruits are small capsules containing numerous small brown seeds in three valves. Northern Swamp Box is found between Weipa and Marlborough in a

variety of vegetation types, including rainforest, but it is generally found in open forest, often along dry watercourses. It makes very good firewood, and Aboriginal people burnt the bark to produce ash that was added to chewing tobacco.

Ht >11m   Lf 30-120mm   Fl Oct-Aug 8-15mm Fr Feb-Mar 4-5mm

Inland Open Forest - Eucalypts

373 Lemon-scented Gum

Eucalyptus citriodora is an attractive gum tree with a pink to orange smooth powdery bark and a strong smell of citrus from the crushed leaves. The trees can be quite irregular in shape, but commonly tall and straight trunked. The older bark is blue grey or pink and sheds in large curling flakes to reveal yellow to orange new bark. The flowers are creamy white, often in groups of three to five, and the fruits are oval to urn shaped, brown, with some raised dots. Lemon-scented Gum occurs between the Windsor Tableland and Maryborough in eastern Qld but is now grown world wide. It produces a valuable oil used in medicine, perfumery, and even in insect repellents. Citronellal is a powerful anti-septic and anti-acterial oil but is poisonous in large amounts. It is often inhaled to ease colds and congestion. The timber is hard and heavy; useful for general construction. It burns well, and makes excellent charcoal. Honey from the flowers is favoured in some African countries.

Ht >40m   Lf 80-160mm   Fl Jun-Nov 12mm   Fr 10-15mm

374 Narrow-leaved Ironbark

Eucalyptus crebra has a dark, almost black, deeply fissured hard bark, and the wood is extremely hard and durable. The foliage is a dull green to blue green, with the leaves narrow and lance-like. The flowers are white, growing in bunches of 7-11 and the fruits are small and hemispherical, often tapering into a short stalk.

Narrow-leaved Ironbark occurs from Cooktown south into NSW, on the coast and inland slopes and plains of eastern Australia. The wood is important as a source of construction timber and railway sleepers. The flowers produce a valuable honey but at a cost to the bees, which must work hard in cool weather to harvest the pollen, yet are not well provided with nutrients for their own use.

Ht >30m   Lf >150mm   Fl May-Aug   Fr 7mm

375 White Mahogany

Eucalyptus acmenoides is a soft barked eucalypt, with a light grey to grey-brown fibrous bark inclined to form strips. The leaves are lance shaped, with dark and light green sides, densely veined. The white flowers are clustered in groups of up to 7 flowers and the fruits are smallish and barrel or urn shaped. These photos were taken at Davies Creek.

White Mahogany occurs from Cooktown almost to Sydney, but only in scattered areas in central Qld. It is a valuable timber tree, producing a hard durable timber favoured for heavy construction such as for bridge and wharf timbers, as well as for flooring, ship building and weatherboards. The flowers are useful for honey production. The wood often contains large holes caused by a wood moth.

Ht >45m   Lf 70-120mm   Fl Oct-Dec   Fr >8mm

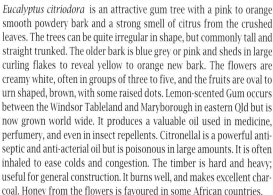

376 Cullen's Ironbark

Eucalyptus cullenii is the dominant tree in the Chillagoe area away from the lime bluffs. The trunks are reasonably straight with a straggly crown (Left), but the deeply furrowed bark, which is often silvery grey, is what attracts attention. The trunks sometimes seem to have a rather conical shape, unusually broad at the base. The wood, and the bark, is very hard. The leaves (>130mm) are alternate, a dull light green or yellowish green, with tightly packed veins. The white or cream flowers grow in groups of from 3 to 7, in bunches on the ends of the branches. The hemispherical gum nuts are quite small, about 4-5mm long.

The tree, which grows to a medium size, is found only in Cape York Peninsula, almost never on the coast. The original 'type' specimen came from near the small railway township of Almaden in 1913.

Lf >130mm   Fr 4-5mm

377 Silver-leaved Ironbark

Eucalyptus shirleyi is one of two similar Ironbarks found on the way to Chillagoe, with dramatic silver-blue foliage (Right). The leaves on young trees wrap around the trunk, forming almost circular pairs. These trees can be seen west of Emu Creek and west of Petford, where they cover many acres.

The Silver-leaved Ironbark is a small rather straggly tree, found only between Mt Mulligan in the Chillagoe area and the Burdekin River southeast of Charters Towers. It is similar to *Eucalyptus melanophloia*, but with a poorer shape and a larger, often ribbed fruit, with white or cream flowers on angular branchlets. The leaves have short stalks when adult and form opposed pairs surrounding the stem. Silver-leaved Ironbark is one of a number of eucalypts that can reproduce while still producing juvenile foliage.

Fl Jan-Apr Fr 12mm

378 Darwin Woollybutt

Eucalyptus chartaboma (prev. miniata) is a small to medium sized tree from Northern Australia which occurs near Chillagoe and Dimbulah. The upper trunk is smooth, and white, pink or yellow, but the butt is covered with pale brown papery bark. The lance shaped leaves can be quite broad, light green and glossy. The flowers are a stunning orange with bright yellow tipped stamens and are followed by very large ribbed fruit with 3 deeply enclosed valves containing large dark grey to black seeds, which fall just before the 'Wet'. The fruits are popular in flower arrangements. The leaf oils have been tested and contain 9 ketones. Native bees often use this tree for their hives.

Lf >160mm Fl Mar-Jul Fr >60mm

Inland Open Forest - Grevilleas

379 Bushman's Clothes Pegs

Grevillea glauca attracts attention on account of its distinctive fruits (Below, Left). The bluish-grey leaves are lightly scattered on the open branches of small trees (>6m) with a dark bark. New growth is a bronze colour. The flowers are similar to the Silver Oak, forming white or cream cylindrical racemes grouped at the ends of branches. They produce copious amounts of an extremely sweet nectar, which can be shaken from the flowers. The two winged seeds are contained in capsules, with their distinctive slot-like openings, which were once used as a substitute for clothes pegs but now are sold as painted 'Happy Faces' in tourist shops and markets. These capsules are used by the Palm Cockatoo to beat on hollow branches, a rare case of a bird seemingly using a tool to make music. The wood may have termicidal properties.

Ht 6-15m   Lf 60-200mm   Fl 60-180mm   Fr 24-40mm

380 Silver Oak

Grevillea parallela gets its name from its long narrow dull green leaves with from 1 to 5 parallel veins visible on the silky hairy underside. This shrub or small tree with hard dark furrowed bark is straggly, but often has an overall balance (Left). The perfumed flowers in bunches of 3-5 racemes, are cream or white, and full of nectar, which attracts a variety of birds. Australia is home to some 357 species of Grevillea, rich in nectar, and many birds have become specialised nectar feeders. The seeds are produced in pairs in a rounded case with a spiny point. Leaves are

sometimes narrowly lobed. Silver Oak is found in a broad band across tropical Australia and extending as far south as Roma in inland Queensland. Near Mareeba this tree grows with the very similar *Grevillea coriaceae*, which has more open clusters of flowers and darker leaves.

Ht 2-5-15m Lf 100-400mm Fl Jul-Dec Fr 20-25mm

381 Beefwood

Grevillea striata is a small open tree of the inland, with broad untidy leaves but similar flower spikes to the Grevilleas above. The tree (>10m) has a short trunk covered with dark grey longitudinally furrowed bark, with a tangle of branches creating an open canopy. The blue-grey, leathery, strap-shaped leaves are some-

what drooping. The cream to yellow flowers occur in summer, and attract many nectar feeding birds and insects. Aboriginal people used the dark-red hard wood for boomerangs in Central Australia, and the leaves helped to heal wounds. A compound known as striatol has been identified and now produced synthetically. It is of interest as a plasma membrane inhibitor. Beefwood is found throughout inland Qld and northern Australia.

382 Hakea

Hakea persiehana is a relative of the grevilleas, and grows a similar small tree. The Hakeas generally have tough, alternate leaves. This species has leaves that are almost needles, producing a thin foliage on a straggly small tree. The flowers are golden, spread along the thin branches where the leaves join and forming extended spikes that are quite attractive (Above). The seed pods (Left) are woody and split to release two thin seeds. Flowering is in Nov to Jan, with seeds following.

These trees can be seen at Emerald Creek Falls and also on the road to Davies Creek where it crosses a small creek only a short distance from the highway. Hakeas are attractive to birds because of the nectar in their flowers and make good garden plants.

383 Hairy Fig

Ficus hispida is found growing in collapsed caves at Mungana near Chillagoe. It is included here to emphasize the difference habitat can make to the form of a plant. Hairy Fig growing in rainforest (see no 226) is so different to the plants shown here that they could well be taken to be two different species. The trees in the caves are large, with substantial trunks and individual figs hang on long stems from the trunks rather than in clusters on a stem. There is much coppice growth around the butts of the trees, with large leaves developing in the low light (Left).

The Sandpaper Fig (see no 105) is another fig that can vary greatly in form, with trees on harsh granite soils small, bare and twiggy in comparison with the lush growth of nearby trees on fertile basalt soils.

384 Rusty Fig (Port Jackson Fig)

Ficus rubignosa can be found at the lookout at Davies Creek Falls, where it is growing on rocks. It also grows as a strangler fig. The leaves (>190mm) can be smooth or somewhat hairy. The name 'rubignosa' means 'rusty red', and refers to the hairs that can grow on undersides of the leaves. The cream point at the end of the branches is known as a stipule (20-130mm) and is very obvious in this species. The fruits can be yellow, red, or orange, pink or purple (7-18mm), in any month, and are eaten by many species of birds.

Many colour variations occur in this fig, including cream and green mottled leaves. It is used as an indoor or garden plant and attracts butterflies and birds. The aboriginal people at Port Jackson (Sydney) ate the fresh fruits or preserved them as a dried cake. This fig is suitable for bonsai.

385 Bakers' Oak (Rose Sheoak)

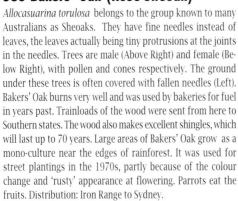

Allocasuarina torulosa belongs to the group known to many Australians as Sheoaks. They have fine needles instead of leaves, the leaves actually being tiny protrusions at the joints in the needles. Trees are male (Above Right) and female (Below Right), with pollen and cones respectively. The ground under these trees is often covered with fallen needles (Left). Bakers' Oak burns very well and was used by bakeries for fuel in years past. Trainloads of the wood were sent from here to Southern states. The wood also makes excellent shingles, which will last up to 70 years. Large areas of Bakers' Oak grow as a mono-culture near the edges of rainforest. It was used for street plantings in the 1970s, partly because of the colour change and 'rusty' appearance at flowering. Parrots eat the fruits. Distribution: Iron Range to Sydney.

Ht >20m   Lf .3-.8mm   Fl Jan&May   Fr Jul-Feb 15-33mm

386 Northern Banksia

Banksia aquilonia is found in open forest close to rainforest or along creek margins. The seedling (Left) is quite distinctive with its radiating serrated edged leaves. New growth (Below) is a decorative whorl of leaves that resembles a flower, especially when it is red or orange. Trees are distinguishable by the whorled

leaves with white undersides, and the pimply bark. The unpleasantly scented flowers are followed by the distinctive cones (Right) which bear the winged seeds. There are 76 species of Banksia, all from Australia and New Guinea, but only Northern Banksia is found in rainforest, between Cedar Bay and Townsville. They are named after Joseph Banks, who as botanist with Captain Cook on the 'Endeavour' in 1770, collected the first specimens.

Ht >25m   Lf 50-220mm   Fl Feb-Jul 25-30mm
Fr cones >120mm

387 Rough Barked Apple

Angophera floribunda is a medium tall Eucalypt-like tree of open forest near Ravenshoe, where it is common. The tree typically has contorted branches with a large crown of light green leaves and the bark is rough and friable on trunk and branches. The leaves taper to a fine lance-like tip, with a prominent midrib and a

stalk 8-12mm long. The flowers are white and the fruits resemble gum nuts with 4 or 5 prominent teeth. Rough Barked Apple is a tree of NSW and SE Qld, with a very isolated population near Ravenshoe. The leaves are suitable for drought fodder and it produces a poor quality honey, though the plentiful blossom is used by beekeepers. The first tree of the genus to be named was apple-like, hence the common name.

Ht >20m   Lf >100mm   Fl Dec-Jan?   Fr 7-10mm

Inland Open Forest - Trees

388 Hooker's Bauhinia

Lysiphyllum hookeri resembles the related Bauhinia, which has a deeply divided butterfly leaf, whereas the Lysiphyllum has a paired compound leaf. The tree is common near Chillagoe, at the northern end of its range, which extends to Dalby in Southern Queensland, as well as the NT. The leaflets are small and dark green. The flowers are white or cream, with pink edges and stamens, unlike the rather similar *Lysiphyllum cunninghamii* which has dull red or brown flowers, and elongated leaves. The flat pods are large. Hooker's Bauhinia is a slow growing, drought tolerant shade tree, which is a great bonsai plant, tending to form a good shape even as a juvenile. It is also known as **Pegunny** or **White Bauhinia**.

Ht >12m   Lf 15-50mm   Fl Jan-Nov   Fr Mar-Apr 60-220mm

389 Turpentine

Syncarpia glomulifera is a medium sized tree in tropical Queensland, growing to a much larger tree further south, where it produces a timber especially useful for marine piles, being resistant to Teredo worm. Although there is a resin in the inner bark which gives it the turpentine odour that distinguishes it, the wood is remarkably difficult to burn. It also contains silica, which blunts tools. The tree is distinguishable amongst other open forest species due to its dark foliage, and small rounded leaves. These are hairy underneath, and new twigs may also be hairy. The white or cream fragrant flowers produce the strange fruits, like small flying saucers, usually with 7 valves These yeild numerous tiny orange-brown seeds. This species has been called the "wood that built Sydney", indicating its importance to early settlers. Piles were exported to London, for use in the docks. As there are 350,000 piles in use in Australia, each worth about $5,000, the value of this resource is quite significant. Turpentine is less resistant to borers in tropical waters, with a life of only 10 to 15 years. The bark produces anti-bacterial chemicals.

Ht >25m in the North   Lf 30-110mm   Fl Aug-Feb 10-16mm   Fr Nov-Jul 10-12mm

390 Mango

Mangifera indica is a native of India and Burma which is now found in rainforest and open forest throughout Cape York and the Cairns hinterland. In open forest Mangoes commonly occur along creek banks, where the trees rapidly grow to around 20 metres in height, and fruit are borne prolifically in Dec to Jan. Most of these trees are what locals would call 'common' or 'stringy' mangoes. Some have a strong turpentine flavour, though most are quite edible. Often the seeds are spread by Flying Foxes, which enjoy the fruits. The simple leaves are aromatic when crushed, with a turpentine smell. New growth is red or pink (Left) and can be quite striking. The fruits are borne on long stems which allow them to hang beneath the branches. Some varieties can spray sap, which stains clothes, for some distance when the fruit is picked. Flowering is variable from year to year, and in a good year the trees are a mass of white blossom. Rain during the flowering season can seriously reduce the crop. Mangoes are a major fruit crop in North Queensland.

Ht > 20m   Lf 100-300mm   Fl Jul-Oct   Fr Dec-Jan 100-150mm

391 Geebung

Persoonia falcata is a small tree or shrub resembling a Grevillea, but with banana shaped flower buds spread along the thin drooping branches. The tree is found from the rainforest to dry areas, often beside rock outcrops. The leaves are long and smooth and radiate around the stems. The flowers have four petals and pro-

duce green fruit in large numbers. The fruits soften when ripe and are edible but astringent with an unusual taste. Aboriginal people used the fruit for food and the hard wood for woomeras, boomerangs, clap sticks and axe handles. The leaves made an infusion for coughs and the bark an eye wash. Geebung seems to be dying out in some areas due to new fire regimes. It occurs widely across northern Australia.

Ht >7m   Fl Jun-Nov   Fr Oct-Mar

392 Prickly Box (Australian Blackthorn)

Bursaria spinosa is one of three Bursaria species in the area, all shrubs or small trees that grow attractive masses of white flowers on thin, thorny stems. Prickly Box flowers from Nov to Apr, and is most likely to be noticed at that time. The smallish blunt ended leaves tend to grow in clusters on the trunk. The flowers have 5 white or cream petals and are scented, followed by purse-like bronze capsules. The shrubs or small trees are usually scattered through an area. In Southern states this plant is known as 'Christmas Bush', due to its time of flowering. It is the host of one of Australia's rarest endangered butterflies, the Bathurst Copper Butterfly, and provides safe nesting sites for native birds. It has been used as a hedge plant and is very hardy, growing in most locations. During WW2 it was used as a source of Aesculin, an alkaloid in the leaves and bark that operates as an effective sunblock, used particularly by the exposed turret gunners in bombers, thus saving the destruction of the Horse Chestnut trees that were previously the only source. Prickly Box grows between Coen and Tasmania, and also occurs in SA and WA.

Ht >10m   Lf 13-43mm   Fl Nov-Apr 6-12mm   Fr Jan-Aug 4-10mm

393 Wild Prune

Pouteria sericea is a rather straggly small tree which is found in vine thickets and littoral rainforest or near rocks in open forest. The tree below is near the Emerald Creek Falls. Often the branches (Right) are coloured bright red, presumedly by a lichen. Aboriginal people sought this tree for its date sized dark purple fruits, which are reputed to be sweet and tasty. Aboriginal names for this tree include

'Wongay' and 'Mangarr' and the wood was used for woomeras and axe handles, as well as for fire-wood. Wild Prune is found from Cape York to Bundaberg, and in the NT and WA.

Ht >8m   Lf 20-140mm
Fl Oct-Jul   Fr Feb-Mar
& Jul-Oct

394 Cypress Pine

Callitris intratropica is an attractive slow growing tree with separate male and female plants. The genus is found only in Australia and New Caledonia. The leaves are tiny, at the joints of the needles, which are adapted stems. The male cones occur at the ends of branches, while the female cones have six valves arranged in a capsule which contains the numerous winged seeds. This species grows in North Queensland, the NT and WA and produces a timber which has many ornamental knots and is resistant to white ant attack. Young trees (Right) resemble European pines. Aboriginal people burned the bark to repel mosquitoes, and a 'blue cypress oil', produced from the heartwood, is used in soaps and cosmetics.

Ht >30m   Lf 1-2mm   Male Cones 3-10mm   Female 10-20mm

395 Brush Cypress Pine

Callitris macleayana is a 'pine' found in and near rainforest in north Queensland. It has a soft blue green canopy and distinctive reddish flaking bark. The tree is common in the wet sclerophyll forests on the western margin of rainforest. The needles are modified stems, and the leaves are small protrusions at each joint of the needle, though young leaves can be 10-15mm long. Male cones are borne singly at the ends of branches, while the female cones can be in groups and are 6 or 8 lobed, containing several brown seeds with a single wing. The cones can be held on the branches for years, releasing seed after a bushfire. The annual growth rings make this a suitable tree for dating. Brush Cypress Pine occurs in northern NSW and SE Qld, and on the Atherton and Mt. Windsor tablelands of north Qld.

Ht >40m Lf 1-3mm Cones 4-8mm (m) 25mm (f)

396 Leucaena (Coffee Bush) (Weed)

Leucaena leucocephala is a small tree or shrub introduced as a cattle fodder plant from Central America, and now naturalised throughout Northern Australia. The tree resembles a wattle, with an open ferny canopy and large brown pods. The leaves are compound, with numerous small leaflets. The flower is a green, cream or yellow pom-pom. The pods are clothed in minute hairs, and contain 8-24 dark brown shiny thin seeds. Leucaena is found throughout tropical Australia and as far south as NSW. It is the most productive tropical legume, and does best on deep fertile soils. The wood is suitable for fuel and charcoal and the green seeds are edible but it is a weed of some concern in many countries, including Australia.

Ht >6m   Lf 5-15mm   Fl Nov-Apr
Fr May-Sep 55-170mm

397 Broad Leaved Bottletree

Brachychiton australis is perhaps the outstanding tree of the lime bluffs near Chillagoe, dominating the scenery (Above) or towering over lower vegetation against the limestone and marble towers. Since this is an area of generally low rainfall, with a long dry season, most plants are small and even this tree rarely exceeds 10 metres. The trunk is pale and smooth, with a slightly bulging appearance that betrays its close relationship to other 'Bottle Trees'. The pinkish-red flowers produce the pod like fruits, packed with bright yellow seeds. These should be handled with care as they are full of tiny irritant hairs. The leaves vary from simple to 3-7 lobed, sandpapery on top and hairy under. New growth is velvety hairy, common to many other Chillagoe plants. The leaf stems are long with swellings at both ends. Broad Leaved Bottletree is found from north of Cooktown to Wandoan in SW Qld. It can be used as fodder in a drought as the leaves are edible. As a garden plant this tree can survive drought and it makes a good bonsai tree.

Ht >10m   Lf 80-180mm   Fl May-Nov   Fr Nov 70-110mm

398 Kurrajong

Brachychiton chillagoensis is a smaller Kurrajong found at Chillagoe, with more rounded leaves than the related Broad Leaved Bottletree (Above). The tree is deciduous (leafless May-Oct), and the leaves are 3-7 lobed, usually sandpapery on top and densely hairy underneath. The leaf stalks are long and swollen at both ends. The flowers are pinkish red with a green base. The pods are similar to *B. australis*

(above) but hold 2-3 dozen brown seeds enclosed in a yellow papery aril which is covered with irritant hairs. The pods open along one side, and can reach 120mm in length. Kurrajong occurs between Chillagoe and Charters Towers in Central Queensland. The bark is strong and fibrous.

Ht > 10m   Lf 90-220mm   Fl May-Nov 25-40mm long   Fr Aug-Jan&Apr 55-120mm

399 Helicopter Tree (Stinkwood)

Gyrocarpus americanus is a Kurrajong-like tree of inland open forest, found with Kurrajongs at Chillagoe. The leaves are not so lobed as the Brachychitons, and the trunk is shiny and reddish-green. The tree is deciduous, with hairy leaves that are entire or 3 lobed, and rather domed, like parachutes. The white, cream or yellow flowers are tiny, with an unpleasant smell.

The fruits have two helicopter wings, giving the tree its common name. Helicopter Tree occurs from Cape York to Mt Blandy in SE Qld and across northern Australia, through SE Asia and the Pacific and in Africa and Central America. The soft, light, grey wood is used for carving and making canoes. It produces analgesic alkaloids and had medicinal uses in India.

Ht >12m Lf 70-240mm Fl Sep-May Fr 50-100mm

400 Weeping Ivorywood

Siphonodon pendulus is a medium sized tree with very long weeping branchlets and a rather dense narrow canopy. The tree reaches 7m in height, and the weeping form is quite distinctive. The trunk can reach a diameter of 300mm. Weeping Ivorywood occurs in tropical northeast Queensland. Flowers are yellow or white. A

small yellow flower can be seen below the fruit in the adjacent photo (Left). The yellow fruits are large and have a hard shell. The bark is dark grey and lightly furrowed. Very little information seems to be available on this rather interesting tree. The tree at right was close to the Red Dome turnoff west of Chillagoe.

401 Cooktown Ironwood

Erythrophleum chlorostachys is a medium sized rounded tree which stands out in open forest due to the dense green of the leaves. The tree is often spreading, offering good shade. The compound leaves are made up of 2 or 3 pairs of pinnae, each with 5-8 rounded leaflets which can be covered in tiny hairs when young. The

flowers are cream, greenish yellow or brown, and the fruits are flat brown or blackish pods containing several flattened seeds with a reddish rim. Cooktown Ironwood occurs from Cape York to Greenvale, and in the NT and WA. The wood is one of the world's hardest and densest timbers. It is milled for timber, and small quantities are used for making flutes. The tree is very poisonous to cattle and horses.

Ht >15m Lf 20-85mm Fl Sep-Nov
Fr Feb-Oct 70-200mm

402 Sims' Wattle

Acacia simsii is a narrow leaved shrub with bright yellow ball flowers borne in ones and twos along the stems where the leaves attach (Right). The leaves taper to each end and can have a little hook on the tip. The leaves of wattles are actually flattened stems, known as phyllodes. There are 3 or 4 prominent veins running the length of these phyllodes. The seed pods, (Left), are distinctive as each second seed in the row protrudes from the pod. This species has been used along roads for revegetation. Sims' Wattle, also known as **Heathlands Wattle**, is found from Cape York to Mackay and extends in a broad band into the NT, also PNG.

Ht 1-4m   Lf 50-110mm   Fl 4mm   Fr >80mm

403 Townsville Wattle

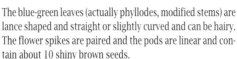

Acacia leptostachya is a modest sized wattle that flowers profusely with bright gold rod-like flower heads that almost hide the leaves. This shrub is widespread in Queensland, from Coen to Chinchilla and Charleville and west to Mt Isa, and can be seen beside the Kennedy Highway at Koah near Kuranda.

The blue-green leaves (actually phyllodes, modified stems) are lance shaped and straight or slightly curved and can be hairy. The flower spikes are paired and the pods are linear and contain about 10 shiny brown seeds.

This attractive wattle is available as a garden plant from specialised nurseries. It is easy to grow.

Ht .5-6m   Lf 40-90mm   Fl Jun-Aug 20-40mm   Fr >60mm

404 Wattle

Acacia whitei is typical of some inland wattles that are low shrubs that hug the ground. This species is only found in three localities in North Queensland; at Davies Creek, near Watsonville, and at Paluma. It commonly occurs on shallow stony soils in rugged hilly areas.

The shrub can reach 2m, though it is usually prostrate. The leaves (phyllodes) are erect, narrow and linear with a prominent mid vein. The branchlets are angular at the ends and red-brown or orange-brown when young.

The flower spikes (5-18mm) are short and yellow and the pods are linear and contain about 10 brown seeds.

Ht >2m   Lf 50-160mm   Fl Mar-Dec   Fr 40-80mm

405 Native Hops

Dodonaea physocarpa is a most attractive hop bush that grows at Emu Creek and around Chillagoe. The bushes are low but loaded with masses of brilliant red and deep pink fruits. The similarity to Hops gives the common name. Dodonaeas are a largely Australian family with 60 of the world's 69 species occurring here (See no 136). They are named after the sixteenth century Flemish botanist Rembert Dodoens. There were Dodoneas being grown in Europe by 1754. Qld, NT & WA.

406 Fart Bush

Breynia cernua is a shrub occasionally reaching 5m height, but commonly 1 to 2m. The common name refers to the unpleasant odour of the crushed leaves, which is a little unfortunate as this is a most attractive shrub with glossy dense green leaves (Right) and pink, red or black berry fruit spread along the branches (Left). It can be pruned to give shapely forms reminiscent of bonsai. The fruits are eaten by pigeons and Lewin's Honeyeaters. It is found in open forest adjacent to rainforest where it forms an understory. The plant appears to have a rather short life of only several years. Fart Bush grows from Cape York to Townsville and also in the NT and through PNG to Malaysia and Melanesia.

Ht >5m   Lf 30-100mm   Fl &Fr any month   Fr 3-12mm

407 Dryander Oak

Grevillea dryandri can be found flowering beside the road to Chillagoe just west of Petford. The plant is quite tiny, with finely divided, grey leaves that are hardly visible amongst the grass. However the flowers are spectacular, the spikes being as long as 300mm, first impressions being that they are bright pink. However they deserve closer scrutiny (Above, Right), as they are full of subtle pinks and mauves, even the stem being purple. The seed pods that follow (Far Right) are very sticky, a distinguishing feature. Most of the world's 362 species of Grevillea are Australian and many birds feed on their nectar. A form of Dryander Oak from near Camooweal has been very successful as a garden plant, but so far the "Herberton" form seen here has resisted attempts to cultivate it. It is found growing on poor, gravelly hills.

Ht >300mm   Lf 60-200mm   Fl Feb-Mar? >300mm spike   Fr 8-15mm

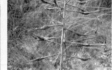

408 Lolly Bush (Butterfly Plant)

Clerodendrum floribundum is a bush or small tree that grows long white flowers and bright red and black fruits. The plant can reach 8m in height, bearing simple leaves on long leaf stalks, which can be red. The prolific fragrant flowers are white or cream and are very elongated. The striking fruits are black, surrounded by a red

calyx (25mm) and contain 4 seeds. Lolly Bush is found from Cape York to Taree in NSW and throughout Central Australia. Aboriginal people used an infusion from the bark and leaves to treat colds and stomach pains. Research has confirmed it's effectiveness as an anti-inflammatory. It is host to the Fiery Jewel butterfly and a moth.

Ht >8m   Lf 65-210mm   Fl any month 20-65mm
Fr Mar-Dec 10-15mm

409 Long Flowered Clerodendrum

Clerodendrum longiflorum resembles Lolly Bush (Above) but with longer flowers and a green rather than black fruit. The plant has smooth, sometimes blue stems, with red or purple leaf stalks. The leaves are simple, dotted with tiny bubble like glands. The flowers are white or cream and the stamens can be very long. The green to purple or black fruit are in a red shiny calyx (20-30mm) and are eaten by many species of bird. Long Flowered Clerodendrum occurs from Cape York to SE Qld, the NT and PNG. It is a host to aphids that form galls on the leaves, which attract several species of ants.

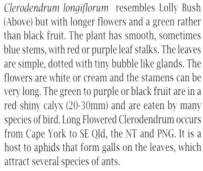

Ht >9m   Lf 40-220mm   Fl Mar-Oct 60-70mm
Fr Mar-Sep 6-10mm

410 Hairy Psychotria

Psychotria loniceroides is a small hairy shrub, common in the wet open forest adjacent to rainforest, and growing small white fruit. The plant has hairy stems, and the leaves are velvety hairy and appear dull on the surface. The white or cream fragrant flowers have 5 petals. The fruits are white, cream or pale yellow, and

attract many birds. Hairy Psychotria is found from Cape York to Bega in Southern NSW, and in the NT and WA. It can be propagated from cuttings, and is sold by some specialised nurseries. It is a host plant of the Hawkmoth, a commercially important insect as it pollinates crops such as Paw paw. Some Psychotrias are poisonous.

Ht >5m   Lf 30-145mm   Fl Apr-Feb 4-7mm
Fr Jan-Jul 3-8mm

Inland Open Forest - Shrubs

411 Anil Indigo

Indigofera suffruticosa is an introduced shrub with pale green compound leaves and spikes of pink pea flowers. The bush is upright or somewhat drooping and the leaves are clothed in pale hairs on the underside. Up to 17 leaflets make up a leaf. The flowers are showy and produce an upright spike of brown pods at any time of year. Anil Indigo comes from tropical America but is naturalised from the Palmer River to SE Qld. This plant is one of the natural sources of Indigo dye and was also the first source of aniline, the basis for many modern dyes. Over a billion pairs of blue jeans are testimony to the popularity of indigo dye, which has been produced synthetically for the last 100 years.

Ht >2m   Lf 10-40mm   Fl Jan-Jul   Fr any month 10-20mm

412 Harnieria

Harnieria hygrophiloides is a deep green shrub with small white flowers that grows in wet open forest adjacent to rainforest. The plant has soft angular stems and carries simple opposed leaves with fine teeth along the edges. The white or cream flowers may show purple dots on the larger, 3 lobed petal. Leaf like bracts sur-

round the flowers, which may be solitary or in clusters. The fruits are green or brown capsules containing 2-4 small brown or black seeds.

Harnieria is also known as **Native Justica**, especially in NSW where it is an endangered plant. It occurs from the Windsor Tableland, west of Mossman, to Brunswick Heads in NSW.

Ht >2m   Lf 25-115mm   Fl Feb-Dec 10-12mm   Fr Apr-Dec 8-10mm

413 Yellow Pittosporum

Pittosporum revolutum is a shrub or small tree of open forest, wet sclerophyll forest and rainforest. The orange capsules open to reveal many red sticky seeds. The bush is often straggly and thinly foliaged in shady locations. The simple leaves can be whorled, and are rusty hairy underneath, with medium sized leaf stalks. The fragrant yellow flowers produce the warty fruits that open to reveal 20-78 sticky red seeds. Satin Bowerbirds and Figbirds feed on these seeds.

Yellow Pittosporum is found from Kuranda to Vic, in a range of habitats, but tending to occur in the wetter areas of the inland open forest.

While the fruit is considered inedible, it is believed that some aboriginal people did eat the bitter contents. Another name for this plant is **Brisbane Laurel**. It is gaining popularity as a garden shrub.

Ht > 6m   Lf 50-220mm   Fl Aug-Oct 9-18mm   Fr Apr-Jul 12-28mm

414 Derris (Butterfly Plant)

Derris sp. (Daintree) is one of four Wet Tropics species of Derris, known to many Australians from its garden use as the insect killer 'Derris Dust'. This species only occurs from Bloomfield to Paluma. Aboriginal people used Derris as a highly effective fish poison. A mass of Derris vine would be rolled into a rough ball, doused in the stream, then beaten with a stick until well broken up. The mass of bruised plant material was then thrown into the pool and the fish would soon come to the surface where they were easily captured. Apparently the poison did not affect the edibility of the fish. It was sometimes known as "wild dynamite", referring to the use of dynamite for killing fish in the early days of white settlement. Derris is a twining vine, with compound leaves and masses of white or pink pea flowers towards the end of the year, followed by thin flat pods bearing one or two seeds, with a prominent vein parallel to one edge of the pod. This plant occurs from the Bloomfield River to Paluma, north of Townsville. It is used by butterflies as a host plant, though the leaves contain saponins.

Lf 65-135mm   Fl Oct-Nov 9mm   Fr Apr-Jul 55-70mm

415 Devil's Twine

Cassytha filiformis is a twining parasite that attaches itself to other plants with tiny suckers. The stems, less than a millimetre in diameter, are yellow-green (Right), or can be orange or dark red. The leaves are barely visible as minute scales. Flowers are green, yellow or white (See Left). The fruits are also unusual, being a small nut surrounded by a fruit (Right) which when fully ripe separates itself to leave just the nut. These fruit are eaten by Lewin's Honeyeaters, Satin Bowerbirds and Crimson Rosellas. Devil's Twine is found around the world, where it is known by names such as 'Love Vine'. It is actually not related to 'Dodder' though closely resembling it. Researchers have isolated at least 17 compounds of medicinal interest from this plant including four aporphine alkaloids which have anti cancer properties. Devil's Twine occurs from Cape York into NSW, also the NT and WA and around the world in tropical regions.

Lf minute scales 1-3mm Fl Aug-Apr 4mm Fr Mar-Sep 4-8mm

416 Cockspur Thorn

Maclura cochinchinensis is a thorny scrambling vine that grows yellow or orange berries. The thorns can be straight or curved and up to 30mm long. The leaves are simple and shiny with medium length leaf stalks. Small green, white or yellow flowers produce the berries which contain numerous brown or black seeds. These are eaten by Lewin's Honeyeaters, Figbirds and Bowerbirds. Cockspur Thorn occurs from Iron Range to Milton, NSW, also through the Pacific and into SE Asia. It contains morin, a compound with powerful anti herpes simplex activity, while several other medicinal compounds have been isolated from the roots. The heartwood produces a yellow dye used in batik.

Lf 20-95mm Fl Sep-Nov Fr Oct-May 15-30mm

417 Gidee Gidee (Poison)

Abrus precatorius is a twining vine that grows vivid red and black seeds in tangles of brown pods. The compound leaves contain 14-38 leaflets. The pea flowers are white, pale pink or purple and the hairy pods each contain from 3 to 7 of the shiny hard seeds. The vine occurs from Cape York to NSW and through most tropical countries, though originating in India. Gidee Gidee is very poisonous. One seed can kill an adult person. The seeds contain a cocktail of over two dozen compounds, the abrins being most dangerous. The root is known as 'Wild Liquorice' in India, but it too is poisonous. The leaves are not poisonous and produce a sweetener. The seeds, our earliest standard weights, are uniform in weight and have long been used to weigh gold and gemstones, and as rosary beads and necklaces.

Lf 5-25mm   Fl Feb-May 8-12mm   Fr Feb-Sep 20-65mm seeds 5-9mm

418 Maesa (Butterfly Plant)

Maesa dependens is a scrambling or twining vine with hairy leaves that produces cream berries. It is found in wet open forest adjacent to rainforest. The leaves are generally hairy on both sides, can be toothed or with a smooth edge, and stand out more or less horizontally from the hairy stems. Small greenish-white flowers are followed by cream, yellow or pink berries with minute orange dots, in loose hanging clusters.

Maesa is found in a small area of North Queensland from Rossville near Cooktown to Ingham, mostly at higher altitude. This genus has its own family, the Maesaceae, with about 100 species worldwide, but only 3 in Australia. This plant is a host to the Miskin Jewel butterfly, and at least two of the 'Blue' butterflies. It has also been the subject of research on changes in leaf size with increasing altitude - the leaves get smaller the higher you go. Tree Kangaroos eat the leaves of Maesa.

Lf 40-120mm   Fl Aug-Nov   Fr any month 4-8mm

419 Rock Rosemary (Weed)

Merremia quinquefolia is an introduced twining vine widely distributed throughout North Queensland. The compound leaves made up of five lance shaped leaflets are carried on long leaf stalks, and can be shiny or edged with fine hairs. The white or cream flowers precede the fruits which are shiny brown capsules containing 4 hairy seeds.

Rock Rosemary comes from tropical America and has become naturalised in North Queensland between Cape York and Rockhampton, occurring in a variety of habitats. The plant photographed was growing on the Walsh River near Dimbulah but this is also a weed of cane fields on the coast. Another name for Rock Rosemary is **Mile-a-minute**, suggesting its invasive growth habit. Rock Rosemary is found in lists of useful herbs from India. It is a weed in Malaysia and Florida as well as in Australia. It is related to the Wood Roses.

Lf 20-65mm   Fl Mar-Nov 10-15mm   Fr Jun-Oct 7-10mm capsules

420 Common Bracken

Pteridium esculentum is one of the commonest plants in Australia where it occurs in all states. The triangular fronds are tall, commonly 2 metres (but >3m) with glossy or dull leaflets that are tripinnate or even quadripinnate (leaflets branch from stems, that branch from stems, that branch...). Common bracken has fine teeth on the leaflets, and the fine hairs under the leaflets are lying down, while the related *Pteridium semibastatum* (Northern Bracken) has smooth edged leaflets with hairs that stand erect. The sori bearing the spores are continuous lines along the margins of the leaflets. Bracken is poisonous to cattle, causing severe vitamin B1 deficiency. Because the underground rhizomes are very hard to eradicate, Bracken is a menace in pastures but is controllable with good management. Despite their hardiness, Brackens are almost impossible to transplant. Aboriginal people ate the poisonous roots after treatment and the new fronds either raw or cooked. However both contain cancer causing compounds. The roots are tough and very fibrous.

421 Maidenhair Fern

Light dictates what can grow in the entrances of caves, or in collapsed caves. At Mungana, west of Chillagoe, there are a number of collapsed caves open to the public, where various plants, including the figs already mentioned (no 383) are growing in semi dark. The Maidenhair ferns (Probably *Adiantum aethiopicum*) (Left) are growing near the entrance to a cave where the light is adequate, and moisture is conserved.

This species of Maidenhair is one of the commonest and best known native ferns, occurring in all states and in most tropical and sub-tropical countries. The species forms extensive clumps, suckering from underground rhizomes. It is very easy to grow. The floating white spot is a spider's web.

422 Algae

Towards the back of the collapsed caves at Mungana, near Chillagoe, the light rapidly diminishes. In this dull half light, often with very stable cool temperatures and high humidity, the conditions suit various algae, which grow on the cave walls or floors. Some walls (Right) are covered with an extremely thin layer of green algae, while nearby (Left) orange and green forms co-exist. These growths are extemely delicate and should not be touched. A footprint in the algae on the ground will last for many months.

There is something ethereal and very soothing about the impact of the green expanse of algae which seems to almost glow in the dull light.

423 Northern Forest Grass Tree

Xanthorrhoea johnsonii is common throughout the open forests of Nth Qld. It is especially noticeable when flowering. The flowers are white and open progressively up the spike, attracting swarms of insects including native bees. The light weight stalks were used by Aboriginal people for spear shafts, and the ruby red gum from the base was mixed with beeswax to glue spears together. The trunks grow 1 metre in 100 years, while the flower spike can grow

30mm in a day. Grasstrees are well adapted to fire. Aboriginees reportedly ate the soft centre of the trunk and the base of the leaves but this plant has poisoned cattle. Grass Trees are found only in Australia, this species from Cape York to Singleton, NSW. 40,000 plants were harvested in Qld in 2003 for garden use.

Ht >4m Lf circa 750mm Fl every 2-3yrs

424 Lomandra

Lomandra hystrix is also known as **Mat-rush**. It is a tough, tufted herb. The ends of the leaves have one prominent tooth. The cream to white spikes of flowers grow in clusters, each with a spiny bract attached. The seeds are designed to be spread by ants, which remove the food body. It belongs to the same family as Grasstrees and is found from Cape York to Taree in NSW. Aboriginal people used the tough strap like leaves for weaving eel traps and coiled baskets. For this reason it is sometimes known as 'Basket Grass'. All 50 species of Lomandra occur in Australia, with some also in PNG and New Caledonia.

Ht >1m   Lf 800-1300mm   Fl Sep-Nov
Fr Jan-May 5mm

425 Spear Grass

Heteropogon contortus is a grass that quickly earns the respect of any careless walker who encounters it. The tangled seeds (Left) are designed to penetrate the soil, but are equally good at moving through clothing and skin. It is advisable to wear gaiters in areas west of the coastal ranges where spear grass is common.

Grazing and disturbance initially increase the growth of spear grass, which is a native pasture grass through much of North Queensland.

The seed is intricately designed. The head is sharp and very hard, and is barbed. The long dark tail has a right angle bend part way along. When the seed is moistened, it begins to twist, and the bent tail prevents it turning, forcing the head into the soil like an auger. If you lick the tail you can watch the seed turn in your hand. Once buried, it is much better able to survive fires. Graziers typically burn spear grass pastures in spring, thereby reducing other plant species. Most spear grass seed is non sexually reproduced, being identical genetically to the maternal plant.

426 Fringed Violet (Fringed Lily)

Thysanotus tuberosus is a stunning small flowering plant with its blue to violet fringed flowers held on a thin stalk only 300-400 mm high. The flowers emerge in the wet season, and the plant seems to favour wet but not waterlogged areas. The flowers open by mid morning and may be wilted by mid afternoon. These were found beside the road West of Petford, in March, amongst Silver-leaved Ironbark trees and associated with Dryander Oak (*Grevillea dryandri* - see no 407). Fringed violets are found across Queensland and NSW and south to Adelaide. They are difficult to maintain in a garden but grow well in containers. Aboriginal people cooked the ground leaves and flowers, and ate the crisp but flavourless tuberous root.

427 Scarlet-flowered Blood-root

Haemodorum coccineum is a perennial plant that flowers after the arrival of the wet season. The plant dies off at the end of the dry season only to re-emerge with the first storms. The underground portion of the plant has a red sap, hence the common name. It favours deep, but moisture retentive, soils. This plant is found near the coast at Cardwell as well as inland near Chillagoe. It occurs across northern Australia and also in PNG.

The Blood-roots are related to Kangaroo Paws and this species with its vivid red flowers is being investigated for the cut flower trade. The plants can lie dormant for several years during a drought, then regrow from the underground structure, or from seed.

428 Bluebells

This *Wahlenbergia* species (poss. *W. queenslandica*) grows in Cape York and resembles Bluebells from other areas of Queensland. It is a soft-stemmed herb growing to about 300mm high and bearing mauve-blue bell-shaped flowers on thin stalks. The leaves are scattered along the base of the stalks, which are lightly branching. These plants mostly occur in grassy or more open areas of the inland open forests.

Bluebells are curious in that they track the sun, the flowers always facing the light. Flowers open during the morning and may close by mid to late afternoon.

Bluebells tend to grow in extensive communities and these commonly occur along road edges.

429 Yellow Everlasting

Xerochrysum bracteatum (prev. Helichrysum bracteatum) is one of a hundred species of 'Everlasting Daisies' found in Australia. There is a great range of varieties, many unnamed, within this single species. The flower illustrated came from dry stony hills near Watsonville. The plants are stunted (>300mm) and the leaves are tiny and hairy, conserving moisture.

Known worldwide as 'Strawflowers' the first Yellow Everlasting plants arrived in England from Australia in 1799. Plant breeders quickly produced a range of colours from white to red and brown. New dwarf forms such as 'Bright Bikinis' are sold as tub plants, but most of the commercial use of this plant has been for dried flower arrangements. Yellow Everlastings belong to one of 80 plant families with extra floral nectaries, which are glands scattered on the plant, not part of the flower, that produce nectar. It is thought that these attract ants which protect the plant against other insects that might harm it. However some recent studies show little advantage from the presence of ants so their purpose is still uncertain.

430 Paper Daisy

Helichrysum newcastlianum is another 'Everlasting Daisy' with finer, somewhat softer petals than the Yellow Everlasting (above). These attractive plants (Left) were growing on the Herberton Range in nearly full sun on rocky banks. Again the plants are small with rather small hairy lance shaped leaves.

There are about 600 species of *Helichrysum* worldwide, with about 100 of those in Australia. Many occur in South Africa. The genus is the source of some argument amongst botanists, many of whom think it is due for a thorough revision.

Paper daisies are referred to as 'Strawflowers' in other parts of the world.

431 Typhonium

Typhonium sp (possibly T. wilbertii) is a small lily like plant with three lobed leaves and an egg cup like receptacle holding the berry like fruit. There are 13 Typhonium species in Australia, with about 4 in the Cairns area. The leaf (80-240mm) of this species is prominently three lobed, the side lobes curved outwards at the base. Leaves are shiny, and emerge each year from an underground tuber, with stems purplish at the base. The flowers (Dec-Jan) are tiny and clustered on a spike which is surrounded by a petal-like spathe, which is green to purple in colour, dark purple inside. The unpleasant smell probably attracts flies. The fruit (Mar-Apr) form at the base of the flowers, and are enclosed by the egg cup shaped base of the spathe. The fruits (10mm) are orange when ripe, and contain one seed.

This plant occurs from Cape York to Cairns.

432 Leafy Hyacinth Orchid

Dipodium ensifolium is a robust and attractive ground orchid that produces masses of pink spotted white to pink flowers in October. This North Queensland native grows erect stems that will over time become long (>1m) and scrambling. The

fleshy roots (>200mm) are deeply embedded in the soil, which may be decomposed granite. The leaves are elongated with prominent veins, the bases overlapping along the stem. The flowers grow on an erect raceme (>550mm).

Leafy Hyacinth Orchid occurs on the coast and also in high areas (eg Herberton) and is listed as rare. It needs plenty of water and sun and may grow in soaks near rocks.

433 Hyacinth Orchid

Dipodium elegantulum is a leafless terrestrial orchid with similar flowers to the Leafy Hyacinth Orchid (above). The flower spike (400-800mm) with dark spotted pink flowers is the only visible part of the plant. The roots are large and fleshy, and live in a symbiotic relationship with a fungus, feeding off rotting wood, hence it will not transplant.

Hyacinth Orchid occurs from the Mt Windsor tableland to near Townsville. Supposedly it can be used to cure insomnia.

434 Pink Nodding Orchid

Geodorum densiflorum is a beautiful small ground orchid bearing pink flowers with paler tips, and red or purple mottling inside. The plant is only 100-250mm tall when flowering, but straightens to 300-400mm tall when fruiting. It has several half buried pseudo bulbs, producing 3-5 pleated leaves each with 3 prominent

ribs. The flowers are held in a spike (150-300mm) on the drooping end of the stem, which straightens to produce fruit. Pink Nodding Orchid is found widely throughout Qld and the NT but is rare in NSW. It also occurs through PNG and SE Asia to India, where it is endangered. In India artificial seeds have been developed from this orchid in a complex process which will allow it to be produced widely.

Ht >400mm   Lf 150-350mm   Fl Dec-Jan 10mm

PLANTS OF STREAM MARGINS

435 Watergum (Kanuka Box)

Tristaniopsis exiliflora is found along streams throughout the area, often with the smooth sinuous trunks overhanging the water (Above). The small white, cream or yellow fragrant flowers and occasional red leaf (Right), are distinctive. Small 3-valved capsules follow. The tree is slow growing and can be buttressed. The leaves are shiny with short stalks and can be alternate or whorled.

Watergum occurs in a small area of North Queensland from the Jardine River near Cape York to Paluma. It is one of three Australian species. The wood is tough, elastic, and close grained, and has been used for tool handles, mallets and planes.
Ht >25m Lf 50-140mm Fl Jul-Dec Fr Jan-Jul 3-4mm

436 Weeping Bottlebrush

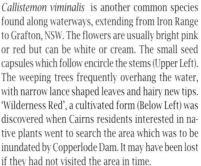

Callistemon viminalis is another common species found along waterways, extending from Iron Range to Grafton, NSW. The flowers are usually bright pink or red but can be white or cream. The small seed capsules which follow encircle the stems (Upper Left). The weeping trees frequently overhang the water, with narrow lance shaped leaves and hairy new tips. 'Wilderness Red', a cultivated form (Below Left) was discovered when Cairns residents interested in native plants went to search the area which was to be inundated by Copperlode Dam. It may have been lost if they had not visited the area in time.

Ht >15m Lf 30-100mm Fl Jun-Feb Fr Feb-Oct 5-6mm

437 African Tulip (Weed)

Spathodea campanulata is a showy tree from West Africa with masses of large, orange to red pea flowers, that protrude from the branches in clusters. These trees have become a weed, especially along waterways from Cairns to Mackay. They are fast growing and difficult to eradicate, as new shoots grow from roots. The bark is rough and a greenish grey-brown and the timber is very soft, like balsa, but attractive with a slight greenish tinge that fades to yellow. The compound leaves are a glossy green and the fruits are dagger shaped woody capsules. The seeds are spread by the wind.

Ht >10m Lf 40-110mm Fl May-Dec Fr 150-250mm

438 Pongamia

Millettia sp (McIlwraith) (previously *Pongamia sp*) has been used as a street tree because of its glossy green leaves throughout the year and its spectacular new growth. It is an attractive small tree of river banks which loses its leaves about Sep and grows a flush of beautiful reddish new growth in Oct (Below). The flowers are small pink pea flowers, hidden in the foliage, and very attractive to insects. They are followed by a green (ripening to brown) flattened pod. These trees can best be admired by taking a river cruise at the time the new foliage is emerging, as they often overhang the water. This is one of two Pongamias in the area; the other, with bigger leaves and fruits, grows only near sea level (see no 53).

Pongamia is found between Iron Range and Mackay and can be seen on the Barron River near Kuranda.

Ht >20m   Lf 35-120mm   Fl Aug-Nov 7-9mm
Fr Oct-Jan 30-45mm

439 Creek Lilly Pilly (Creek Cherry)

Syzygium australe is one of about 50 species of Syzygium found in North Queensland. They mostly bear edible fruits, which may be quite tart to taste, but which make good jellies and jams. (You should not sample native fruits unless you are quite sure of the species; many are poisonous.) This species is found along creeks and rivers in and out of rainforest. The flowers, masses of white stamens, occur throughout the year, followed by the pink or red fruit. Immature fruit are green (Right, below). Often the fruit are found floating on the water in

streams, from which they can easily be scooped. The plop of falling fruit is a familiar sound under a fruiting tree. The tree grows shiny leaves on short stalks.

Creek Lilly Pilly occurs from Bloomfield to Nowra in NSW, and the fruits are eaten by King Parrots, Wompoo Fruitdoves, Figbirds, Bowerbirds, Lewin's Honeyeaters and Brush-turkeys.

Ht >24m   Lf 30-100mm   Fl any month Fr any month 14-23mm

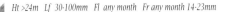

440 White Apple

Syzygium forte is a medium sized tree that grows bunches of large berry-like white or cream fruit. The tree grows on the coast, in rainforest, or along streams between Cape York and Ingham, and also in the NT and PNG. The rounded leaves are simple with moderately short stalks. The white or cream flowers are about 6mm across, and the fruits contain one large seed. These fruits are eaten by Cassowaries and Spec-tacled Flying Foxes. The leaves and fruits from this tree are also eaten by the Pig-nosed Turtle. This plant is sold as an attractive garden species with glossy leaves and bright red new growth producing crunchy edible fruit. (Do not eat fruit from native plants unless you are sure of them - similar fruits may be poisonous.)

Ht >30m Lf 60-165mm Fl Sep-Dec 6mm Fr Nov-Apr 30-47mm

441 River Cherry (Butterfly Plant)

Syzygium tierneyanum is common along streams in rainforest and nearby areas, growing masses of small red or white fruit that have four protruding lobes on the ends. The tree may be buttressed, with dense foliage, the simple, shiny leaves carried on short stems. Masses of white or cream blossom attract the Day Flying (Zodiac) Moth, which may be mistaken for a large butterfly. The fruits each contain

a large seed, but the tart flesh makes a pleas-ant jam or jelly. Cassowaries eat the fallen fruit. River Cherry grows between Cape York and Paluma near Townsville, and is found in PNG. One flowering tree under study was visited by 7 species of birds, 9 species of but-terflies, 12 kinds of moths, 2 bees, 2 ants, 1 wasp, 3 blowflies, 1 fruit fly, 2 beetles, a weevil and a species of bat.

Ht >25m   Lf 90-190mm   Fl Oct-Feb
Fr Jan-May 15-20mm

442 Glue-berry Tree

Cordia dichotoma (Right) is a smallish tree found in rainforest and also along stream banks in open forest. It may be buttressed. It is one of five species of Cordia in North Queensland, most of which grow fruits which are filled with a very sticky flesh. The pink fruits (10-23mm) have a pearly lustre and are the size of small grapes, containing a few small brown seeds within the clear sticky mucilage. In India the fruits are eaten raw, or green as a vegetable, along with the leaves. Pick-led fruit are sold in Taiwan. (Do not eat fruits you are not completely sure of - many are poisonous). Various medicinal com-pounds have been isolated from the leaves and anti-inflammatories from the seeds. Glue-berry Tree occurs between Cape York and Bundaberg, in the NT, and through PNG to SE Asia and India.

Ht >20m Lf 35-210mm Fl Sep-Oct Fr Sep-Jan

443 River Oak

Casuarina cunninghamiana is a tree of river and stream banks with a dark foliage and trunk. The needle like 'leaves' are actually adapted stems. The true leaves are tiny protrusions at the joints in these stems. The tree is the largest species of Casuarina in Australia. River Oak typically grows between normal water level and

the high flood level on stream banks. The male flowers grow on the tips of branches, while the female flowers develop into the distinctive ribbed cones. River Oak occurs between northern Cape York and southern NSW, also in the NT, where there is a different race. The pinkish-grey wood has marked rays resembling English Oak. The tree is of value in preventing erosion on stream banks.

Ht >35m Lf 8-10 .1mm teeth/whorl

444 Jam Jam

Buchanania arborescens is a tree of rainforest and open forest, commonly found on stream banks where it can closely resemble the related Mango (no 390). The tree carries simple elongated leaves often in whorls at the ends of the branches. Small white or cream flowers with 5 or 6 petals are followed by small mango-like

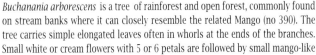

fruits that ripen to red or black. These fruit are eaten by fruit doves, Metallic Starlings and Fawn-breasted Bowerbirds. Jam Jam occurs from Cape York to Ingham, and in the NT and WA, as well as through PNG to SE Asia. Jam Jam is being marketed as a garden tree with dark glossy leaves and attractive red new growth, bearing "small, pleasant tasting globular fruit". (Do not eat unfamiliar fruits - they may harm you.)

Ht >25m Lf 50-260mm Fl Jul-Oct 6-8mm
Fr Oct-Jan 9-12mm

445 Maytenus

Maytenus fasciculiflora is a small tree or shrub which produces large crops of yellow fruit clustered on the stems. It is found in rainforest on the coast and in open forest along streams. The tree is bushy and branching, with shiny leaves on short stalks. Tiny green, white or cream, fragrant flowers produce masses of yel-

low, orange or red fruits which are two valved and enclose 1 or 2 cream, yellow, brown or black seeds. This Maytenus is one of five species in the area, out of the 10 Australian species. It is found from near Cape York to the Mulgrave River. The tree photographed is on the banks of the Annan River near Cooktown, the same area from which the original botanical specimen was collected.

Ht >8m Lf 30-120mm Fl May-Aug
Fr Jan-Jun 5-7mm

446 Cook's Screw Pine

Pandanus cookii is named after James Cook, the English navigator who first sailed up the East coast of Australia in 1770. It is a tall Pandanus growing in a variety of forest types and along stream banks. Those at left were growing above the falls on Davies Creek. The tree has short prop roots at the base and can carry dense erect aerial roots (>100mm) on the trunk. The leaves are a whitish green and arranged in a spiral around the trunk. There may be a few spines near the base of the leaves on the edges but the midrib is spineless. The fruits are orange or red and are eaten by Palm Cockatoos. They have fewer teeth per segment than the Swamp Pandan (no 81) which differs in having spiny conical nodules on the trunk and darker leaves.

There are about 700 species of Pandanus worldwide, of which about 20-40 (depending on the classification used) occur in Australia. Some 14 species can be found in the Wet Tropics area. Cook's Screw Pine is found between Cape York and Mackay, up to an altitude of about 500m.

Ht >10m   Lf 1.3-1.8m   Fl a terminal spike   Fr Nov-Mar 200-300mm

447 Navua Sedge (Weed)

Cyperus aromaticus is an introduced sedge from tropical Africa and Madagascar, which is becoming a weed of wet areas in North Queensland. This clump forming sedge grows leaves from the base of the plant and has 5-7 leaf-like bracts radiating from the top of the flowering stalk. These can be from 80 to 200mm in length. It grows best in moist fertile soil in full sun.

Although a declared weed in Queensland, this sedge has potential to produce a

third generation bioinsecticide, which mimics the juvenile hormone in insects. This would be a safer and more environmentally friendly form of insecticide than those on the market.

Ht 200-500mm   Lf >150mm
Fl 7-12mm head of 4mm spikelets

448 Umbrella Sedge

Cyperus alternifolius is an introduced sedge which originates from the swamps of Madagascar and Mauritius. It is an attractive plant about 1 metre in height, favouring light shade to full sun adjacent to water. This plant (Left) was growing on Jum Rum Creek in Kuranda.

The grass like leaves radiate from the top of the stems. Flowers are borne on long thin spikes which also radiate like the spokes on an umbrella, but are rather insignificant, small and greenish brown in colour and followed by small seeds.

Umbrella Sedge can reproduce small plantlets from the tops of the stems, provided it is very humid or the head is touching the water. This means that the plant can become invasive in some situations. It is grown around the world as an ornamental, and the leaves are used in floral arrangements. There are variegated, compact and dwarf forms. It is a clumping plant with clumps up to one and a half metres across. It is quite closely related to the Papyrus of the Nile River.

Stream Margins - Orchid & Sundews

449 King Greenhood

Pterostylis baptistii is one of a large family of small terrestrial orchids. The rosettes of leaves grow close to water in creeks emerging from rainforest, and the striking hooded flowers were seen in June. The plants are perennial, with the rosettes of leaves forming from an underground tuber before the flower spike emerges. The plant can grow to 250mm tall with a flower 60mm long. Greenhoods have developed an interesting mechanism to assist with pollination, which is carried out by male gnats and mosquitoes. An insect entering the flower chamber triggers a trapdoor, which springs closed, trapping it inside. To get out, the insect climbs a column to the top of the flower, where it escapes, carrying the pollen to fertilize the next flower it enters.

While the greenhood shown grows in granite derived soil, many seem to thrive in leaf mould and are hardy enough to respond well to fertilizer. King Greenhood is found in coastal Qld and NSW and is a rare plant in Vic.

450 Tall Sundew

Drosera auriculata is a straggly sundew found close to water in streams emerging from rainforest. The thin stem is erect (150-700mm) and has a rosette of insectivorous leaves (30-100mm) at the base and then alternating along the stem. Each leaf consists of a cone shaped central core, surrounded by an aura of fine hairs tipped with shiny drops of a sticky liquid. Any small insect that touches the hairs becomes trapped and the hairs then fold inwards bearing the insect into the core of the leaf where it is digested by the plant. In the infertile soils where these plants grow the nutrients derived from insects are an important source of nutrition for the plant. The flowers are large and white or pink (Jun-Nov), with flowering often continuing while conditions are moist. Plants grow from an underground tuber and appear to live for several years.

Tall Sundew is found in eastern Qld and NSW, extending into Vic and growing from sea level to high altitude (1100m). *Drosera auriculata* was previously known as a subspecies of *Drosera peltata*.

451 Woolly Sundew

Drosera petiolaris is not really a sundew of streambanks, tending to grow on bare patches of soil or sand that can become quite dry, though it prefers damp areas. Woolly Sundew is a fibrous rooted perennial herb (>200mm) forming leafy rosettes. The flowers are white or pink (Aug-Oct & Jun-Apr) and the flower stalks and

leaf stalks can be covered with woolly hairs. Insects that get entangled in the sticky hairs create vibrations that cause the hairs to turn inwards. The insect is digested by the plant's enzymes in the cup-like leaf. Woolly Sundews are adapted to very hot and wet summers and thrive across tropical Australia. There are many species of sundew in Australia and a number are closely related to Woolly Sundew. Plants grow from seeds or detached leaves.

Water Plants

452 Native Water Hyacinth

Monochoria cyanea is an attractive native plant resembling the invasive introduced Water Hyacinth. The plant (>450mm) is perennial in permanent water, with heart shaped leaves (40-150mm) emerging from the water on long stems. The stems form roots on contact with the soil. The six petalled blue flowers (20-40mm) with yellow stamens occur from Dec to Apr, and several flowers are borne on an upright spike (>130mm). The fruits are 3-valved capsules containing numerous seeds. Water birds eat the seeds and the leaves are edible. Native Water Hyacinth is found across most of Qld, through inland NSW and the NT (a threatened species in both) and in northern WA. It is one of four native Australian species of Monochoria, with only six species worldwide.

453 Giant Waterlily

Nymphaea gigantea is a native waterlily that occurs across coastal Queensland but is more common in the north, where it grows in still water up to 1.5m deep. The leaves are rounded (100-600mm) with regularly spaced teeth (>4mm) around the margin. The edges of the leaf often overlap along the line of the basal split. The fragrant flowers (>250mm) vary from dark purple to blue to white, the petals having rounded tips. The bright yellow stamens turn inwards towards the centre of the flower. The flowers are held above the water on stout stalks. Flowering occurs over the Summer and Autumn months. The large oval fruit capsule (75mm wide) matures underwater and produces numerous seeds with a red coat.

Giant Waterlily is also found in northern NSW and in the NT. Aboriginal people ate the root, stems and fruit. The tuberous roots were eaten raw or roasted, the stems (sometimes known as the 'rope') could be eaten raw and the seeds either eaten raw or pounded on stones and baked into small cakes. The leaves may prevent leeches when rubbed on the body. The photograph is from Keatings Lagoon near Cooktown.

454 Salvinia (Major Weed)

Salvinia molesta is an introduced weed from South America. It floats on the surface of water and can form vast expanses of vivid green leaves. It is actually a fern, and thrives on still or slow moving water, but can survive in wet mud for some time. The leaves are in groups of three, two floating leaves that are succulent, light green and showing a prominent mid rib, and one submerged leaf that is brownish coloured, deeply divided and root-like. The floating leaves are covered in curved, water-repellent hairs. There are no flowers, but spores are produced all year. Most reproduction is by fragmentation of the stems. Salvinia taints water, blocks pumps and pipes, and prevents stock drinking. Reducing nutrients in the water helps prevent it and a weevil from Brazil attacks it.

Weeds

455 Blue Top

Ageratum conyzoides is a common weed of waste ground, forming almost a total cover in many areas. The lovely violet blue flowers top a herb less than a metre tall, with opposed hairy leaves (20-100mm) which are a dark glossy green. Flowers can also be white or pink.

Blue Top originates from tropical America and grows from Cape York into NSW and in the NT. It is reported that a paste made from the roots is effective in controlling evil spirits.

456 Pink Snakeweed (Butterfly Plant)

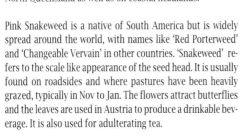

Stachytarpheta mutabilis is a shrub growing to 3 metres, with 5 ribbed hairy stems and velvety hairy leaves. The seed heads (Right) are erect and curving rather than straight, bearing bright pink, purple or red tubular flowers (Left). This plant is found around Kuranda and on the Atherton Tablelands in North Queensland as well as on coastal headlands.

Pink Snakeweed is a native of South America but is widely spread around the world, with names like 'Red Porterweed' and 'Changeable Vervain' in other countries. 'Snakeweed' refers to the scale like appearance of the seed head. It is usually found on roadsides and where pastures have been heavily grazed, typically in Nov to Jan. The flowers attract butterflies and the leaves are used in Austria to produce a drinkable beverage. It is also used for adulterating tea.

457 Dark Blue Snakeweed

Stachytarpheta cayennensis is closely related to Lantana (no 141) and Pink Snakeweed (Above) and also comes from tropical America. It has similar growth habits to Pink Snakeweed, and can form large masses of plants on disturbed ground. The flower colour varies from violet/purple to blue.

In its home territory there are many traditional medicinal uses of Snakeweed (also known as Blue Rat's Tail). It contains salicylic acid, the precursor of Aspro, and seems to be effective against worms and parasites, helps with liver conditions, and, as a broncodilator, can assist respiratory problems. In some cultures it was used to stimulate menstruation. It has also been used externally to clean ulcers, cuts and wounds. It is, however, a problem weed in French Polynesia. It is found between Cape Tribulation and Brisbane in Australia.

458 Singapore Daisy (Weed)

Sphagneticola trilobata is another Central American native which has become a significant weed in North Queensland. It has been used as a ground cover, but tends to overrun native vegetation, including small trees and shrubs, forming a dense mass of vegetation. As it propogates from nodes, it is hard to eradicate. The 30mm bright yellow-orange daisy like flowers (Right) are attractive against the dark green toothed leaves (30-200mm) in pairs along the stems. It does not tolerate deep shade and needs plenty of water, preferring sandy soils. It is naturalised from Cape York to Byron Bay in NSW, and is a major weed around Kuranda.

459 Red Passion Flower

Passiflora coccinea grows brilliant scarlet red flowers, (Below), on roadsides and waste ground near rainforest. It is a native of the tropical American lowlands that has become common as a weed in the local area. It is a tendril climber and the tendrils are visible (Left) twining around vegetation. The leaves are usually simple, without lobes, and the flowers are large and striking (70-120mm), lasting only one day and closing in rain. The fruit is an edible green/yellow/orange mottled hard capsule, rarely seen locally. This plant is reported to attract butterflies, and is also known as **Scarlet Passionflower**. Do not eat fruits that you are not confident of. Many can harm you.

460 Sensitive Weed

Mimosa pudica is an unusual plant that reacts to touch, warmth or shaking. The leaves quickly fold down, exposing the thorny stems. They also fold at night. This is due to a rapid loss of pressure in certain cells, though the full mechanism is not yet fully understood. Sensitive Weed is a prostrate herb that can scramble over other vegetation, with stems (>1.5m) and compound leaves slightly hairy. The pink pom-pom flowers (Right) appear from Dec to Jul, followed by flat, hairy, brown pods containing from 2 - 6 seeds. Sensitive weed is a native of Brazil now widespread in Australia from Iron Range to central NSW, favouring roadsides and mown areas. It has a deep taproot, and a proportion of its seeds will lie dormant in the soil to germinate years later, making it a difficult weed to eradicate. All parts of the plant are toxic and it contains many medicinal compounds (including mimosine) with antibiotic, antimicrobial, antidepressant and sedative effects.

Weeds

461 Castor Oil Plant

Ricinus communis is a poisonous weed of roadsides, waste land and watercourses. The plants reach 2.5m or more in height. The hollow stems are a dull, pale green in colour, with the large leaves (>300mm) widely spaced on the branches. Each leaf is composed of several segments, with prominent mid veins, radiating from a long,

hollow leaf stalk. New leaves are reddish-brown, glossy, with a sickening smell when crushed. The orange flowers are on spikes at the top of the plant, producing fruit (25mm) covered in red or green soft spikes, which turn brown and explode violently when ripe. Each of the three segments produces one smooth seed. These produce a medicinal or industrial oil. A familiar and dangerous medicine; 3 seeds can kill a man. Castor Oil is an alternative energy plant.

462 Golden Dewdrops

Duranta erecta is a bushy shrub which bears pale blue flowers and bright yellow/orange berries throughout the year. The plant can reach 5m in height and can carry spines from 5-20mm long. The leaves (25-50mm) can be simple or toothed, on short stalks. The 6-10mm fragrant flowers occur on rather drooping branches all year, and are blue or purple. The fruits are attractive to many birds and this plant now occurs in isolated areas where presumedly birds have carried the seeds. It is becoming an increasing problem as a weed of rainforest edges. Unfortunately the plant is still sold as a garden plant, though there are new varieties which are supposedly unable to set viable fruit. Golden Dewdrops can be found between Cooktown and NSW, also in the NT. It came originally from tropical America. While the flowers are attractive to butterflies, the fruits are poisonous to humans.

463 Rubber Vine (Major Weed)

Cryptostegia grandiflora is a wide-spread major weed of tropical Australia. The vine (>50m) can climb high into trees or form shrubs (1-3m) in the open (Right). The tough vine forms impenetrable thickets, and it has covered large areas of central and northern Qld, especially along the Gulf rivers, as well as occurring in the

NT and WA. The paired glossy leaves (60-100mm) may have purple veins, and all parts of the plant produce a milky sap that yeilds rubber. White to light purple trumpet shaped flowers (>50mm) produce pods (>120mm) on older plants which produce up to a million brown seeds per hectare, each with white silky hairs. The vine, from Madagascar, reduces productivity and replaces native species. It can be controlled by burning and spraying.

Weeds

464 Cusara Pea

Crotalaria zanzibarica (Left) is an annual weed with yellow flower spikes and leaves with three leaflets. The plant grows to 2 metres, with lance shaped leaflets (70mm). The bright yellow flowers with red stripes and purple blotches are held on erect spikes and are followed by pods (>30mm) containing numerous orange seeds.

Cusara Pea is a common weed of roadsides and headlands, extending as far south as Brisbane. Several Crotalarias are introduced weeds in Queensland.

465 Streaked Rattle Pod

Crotalaria pallida (Right) is related to and resembles Cusara Pea (Above) but has rounded leaves, dark green but yellowing with age, on a shorter (600-1200mm) bush. The pods (50mm) contain 30-40 light brown seeds which rattle in the pod.

466 Bellyache Bush (Major Weed)

Jatropha gossypifolia is a rather striking bush with three lobed leaves which are a deep purple-red when young. The scientific name indicates that the leaves (>100mm) resemble those of cotton. The shrub (>2m) is squat with thick stems, and the leaf margins and stems carry short coarse hairs with sticky glands. The flowers (Jan-

Mar) are red with yellow centres, clustered at the tips of the branches. The seed capsules (12mm) are 3 lobed containing seeds about 8mm long. These are ejected with such force they can travel up to 12 metres from the bush. Bellyache Bush is a major weed in tropical Qld, poisoning stock and killing native vegetation. It contains medicinal compounds with anti-coagulant and anti-bacterial properties and is a potential bio fuel. It contains much more sugar than sugarcane, but is also poisonous.

467 Khaki Weed

Alternanthera pungens is a low growing weed that forms mats of sharp prickles that adhere to feet, clothing and tyres. This is a perennial plant with a deep tap root. The stems root at the nodes, and form a carpet over large areas. The leaves (12-37mm) are dull green, on short stalks, and flowers form in each leaf junction in

dense clusters. The cream petals end in sharp points that dry to become the prickles. Khaki Weed is widespread throughout Qld, especially on roadsides and in old cultivations. Sometimes, as in the photograph from near Mt Carbine, it spreads into pastures. While a most irritating weed due to the masses of prickles, it does not have a great economic impact and small areas can be controlled by chipping, or by spraying when young.

Ornamental Trees

ORNAMENTAL TREES AND SHRUBS

This section includes some of the more striking street trees and ornamental trees likely to be seen in the Cairns area. Mostly they are exotic plants, imported for their beauty, but a few are local. This selection focusses on trees and some large vines, and does not include the hundreds of striking garden plants that are available in the Tropics. A visit to the Botanic Gardens in Collins Avenue will reward those with an interest in exotic plants.

468 Poinciana (Christmas Tree)

Delonix regia comes originally from Madagascar, but is found throughout the tropics as a striking flowering tree. Because it flowers at Christmas time and the contrast between the red flowers (Right) and green leaves mimics the Christmas colours of red and green, it is sometimes known as the **Christmas Tree.** The tree is very spreading (Above) and a 10 metre high tree can be over 20 metres across. There can be up to 2400 fine leaflets in one compound leaf. The trunk has interesting flanges at the points where branches join. After the flowers fall the tree is loaded with large flat pods (>500mm), which can be a nuisance. The timber can be used for sculpting, taking advantage of the unusual shapes in the branches, but the wood is a horrible bilious yellow colour that gradually fades to a yellow brown.

Poinciana can form single species stands, and has potential to become an environmental weed in Australia. Its pods were used in the Carribean as the original maraca. Blooming improves with age and also is better after a dry spell.

469 Frangipani

Plumeria obtusa is one of several species of Frangipani found in North Queensland. It comes from Singapore, while some of the coloured varieties come from Central America. The perfume is strong and exotic and the flowers are strung on strings to form necklaces or leis in some Pacific Island communities. They form part of a traditional greeting in Hawaii. There is a current fashion for large flower paintings of Frangipani for sale in tourist centres like Cairns. The tree is small, generally below 8 metres, with radiating whorls of the dark green leaves, which can reach 180mm in length. The flowers (Left) are clustered at the ends of the branches. The trunk is a rather straggly affair, and when the plants lose their leaves it looks rather pathetic. However, a branch broken from a Frangipani tree can lie on the ground for months and then take root and grow. The variety with a larger yellow centre is used in India in temples. There are also pink, red and gold varieties.

470 Trumpet Tree

Tabebuia chrysantha is reputed to have the brightest yellow flower known. It comes from Nicaragua, where it is the national tree. A deciduous tree, it flowers in Cairns in November. In flower, it forms a mass of dazzling blooms with foliage not visible.

The genus also provides a number of the largest and most valuable timber trees in South America, providing excellent wood for decking. Contact with the sawdust, though, can cause dermatitis.

471 Cassia (Cascara, Golden Shower)

Cassia fistula bears masses of bright yellow flowers (Dec-Feb) which hang in long festoons from the rather open branches (Left). It is a fast growing tree which can reach a height of more than 5 metres in just 7 years, and produce flowers in 3 or 4. The flowers are followed by sausage shaped pods 300mm or more long, with a sharp point that sometimes allows the falling pod to dig into the ground. The tree often flowers before the leaves have developed, making for a more striking display. It is deciduous in winter.

472 Pink Cassia

Cassia javanica and *Cassia nodosa* are pink forms of Cassia, taller growing than *Cassia fistula* and less showy as the flowers are borne amongst the leaves. They flower in Jan. The tree illustrated (Right) is probably *C. javanica,* which, as the name suggests, is a native of Indonesia. It is also known as **Apple Blossom Cassia** and **Pink Shower Tree**.

The tree grows to about 17 metres, and the leaves are composed of 12 paired leaflets. It is grown around the world in tropical areas for its flowers. *Cassia nodosa* is a rather similar tree with similar growth habits. This tree was growing in a park in Edge Hill, Cairns.

Ornamental Trees

473 Jacaranda

Jacaranda mimosaefolia is a flowering tree from north-western Argentina, which has thrived in Australia. The lavender/blue flowers hang on the often bare branches in Oct, creating beautiful displays. As older trees in dryer areas produce the best flowers, local residents will often visit towns like Herberton, once the 'capital' of North Queensland, just to view the blossoms throughout the town.

Jacarandas grow into large spreading trees (>16m). The light coloured wood is suitable for cabinet making and carving, the dark bark adhering well for contrast.

474 Golden Penda

Xanthostemon chrysanthus is a common street tree in Cairns, being the floral emblem of the city. Many have been planted in median strips on approaches to Cairns. It is an Australian native plant, originally found only in the Wet Tropics of Queensland, along with 12 other Penda species. (Visitors to Kuranda can see the Giant Pendas on the way to the Barron Falls, though their location is currently not well marked, and you may need to get directions to find them.) Golden Penda has the most showy flowers (Left), which form heads larger than your hand. The name 'Xanthostemon' means 'yellow stamens'. Flowers (Feb-Nov) occur as a mass flowering, with the fruit, a brown capsule, following. Fruit are visible at the top of the photograph (Left). While most of the Pendas are small rainforest trees, this species grows to 25 metres. As a garden plant, the Golden Penda can be pruned to shrub size and will flower in only 2-3 years. Golden Penda is found from Ingham almost to Cape York. A cultivar known as 'Expo Gold' was developed for the World Expo in Brisbane in 1988. The potential for cut flower development is being explored.

475 Rain Tree

Samanea saman is grown not so much for the flowers (Inset) but for the foliage. These trees create huge canopies which offer dense shade in the heat, but which have leaves that fold up at night or during rain, hence the common name of 'Rain Tree'. The tree is common throughout Cairns and Kuranda, but possibly the finest specimens are located on the northern outskirts of Mossman. The tree (Right), planted by the author, is only 16 years old, but already has a spreading canopy. The Rain Tree comes from Mexico and there are concerns that it could develop into a weed, especially in the Daintree area. It produces a beautiful dark brown timber.

Ornamental Trees

476 Flame Tree

Brachychiton acerifolius is a native of Australia, found in rainforest from Iron Range on Cape York to central New South Wales. The brilliant red flowers are borne on leafless branches, which increases the intensity of their impact. As the tree can grow to 45 metres, flowering trees are often visible for miles in the rainforest. At the same time, it is possible to walk directly underneath such a tree without suspecting it is there, unless fallen flowers are seen on the ground. The trunk is often pale in colour and somewhat corky in appearance, with a smooth or pimply surface. Juvenile leaves, (Left), are lobed, hence the name 'acerifolius' - 'having leaves like Maples'. Flowering occurs Sep to Jan, and the brown to black seed capsules follow, sometimes remaining until the new flowering (Right). The capsules contain numerous fine irritant hairs, and should be handled with care. These trees are common throughout the region as ornamental trees and those photographed were in Cairns, the pair above in a park at Edge Hill.

477 Bougainvillea

Bougainvillea glabra is a thorny climbing plant from South America. It can grow as a vine or form a clump with a robust stem at the base. The 'flowers' are actually the flower bracts, which are coloured red, pink, purple or white, with a number of bi- and multi coloured forms available. These are robust plants which send up long thorny tendrils (Left). The spines on these can be quite long, and inflict a painful wound. The plants are often pruned into standards or hedges. Although they require care to establish, once grown they are very hardy. It is common to find clumps of Bougainvillea that have survived both drought and fire over many years in abandoned mining towns.

Ornamental Trees

478 Silky Oak

Grevillea robusta is an Australian native tree from Southern Queensland and North/Central New South Wales. The timber has a strong 'oak' grain and is used for cabinet making. The tree grows ornamental orange flowers (Right) which attract birds, and the deeply divided leaves with silvery undersides are also attractive. These trees may not have a long life in the humid tropics, though some grow to a large size. The toothbrush-like flowers (Oct) produce brown to black 15-19mm pods.

479 Bauhinia

Bauhinias have 'butterfly' leaves and bear orchid-like white, purple, red, mauve and pink flowers (Left). Trees (>12m) flower at various times, commonly about Mar. The leaves of Bauhinia are deeply divided and can fold together at night (Below). There is some doubt over the origins of a Bauhinia species found near Cairns - it is probably introduced, possibly from China.

480 Allamanda

Allamanda cathartica is a sprawling, climbing shrub from Guyana and Suriname which grows large bright yellow flowers in summer (Right). *A. violacea* is a purple flowering form (Left). Allamandas do best in rich, damp soil in warm climates. They are often grown over fences or walls. The plant will grow up to 3 metres tall, and the flowers can be 120mm across. Related to the Oleanders, Allamanda has a white sap and all parts of the plant are poisonous. The roots were used to treat jaundice and the flower used as a laxative. The plant has antibiotic properties. In north Queensland it is becoming an invasive weed.

481 Swamp Bloodwood

Corymbia ptychocarpa is a small to medium sized 'Eucalypt' from the Northern Territory and northern Western Australia that is widely grown as an ornamental tree. It grows large bunches of pink, red, apricot or (rarely) white flowers, often in groups of seven. Flowering is followed by the setting of large ribbed gumnuts (see photo, Right) containing the red/brown winged seeds. The leaves are very large, closely veined and glossy. The bark is rough and fractured and a brownish grey colour. In their native habitat Swamp Bloodwoods are scattered and always found along creeks or in damp sites, such as seasonal swamps.

Popular garden plants because of the bright flowers and relatively small size of the tree, Swamp Bloodwoods do not always retain the colour of the tree from which seed was taken. They are sometimes grafted and recently a cross between this and a West Australian flowering gum has produced vivid hybrids.

Ht 8-15m   Lf 160-250mm >70mm broad   Fl Sep-Mar Fr 35-60mm

482 Cannonball Tree

Couroupita guianensis is an exotic tree from Guyana, a native of the Amazon rainforests. The large pink, red and yellow flower (Right) is pollinated by bats, and is very fragrant. The fruits (Left) are large and woody, containing small seeds in an unpleasant smelling white jelly, supposedly edible. The shells of these fruits are used as containers.

In the Amazon the tree can reach a height of 25m with huge 2 metre long leaves. The flowers are cauliflorous, meaning they grow directly on the trunk. Stems are covered with spiny protuberances, and the tree has a straggly look. One is growing on the Esplanade in Cairns and another is beside the road to Crystal Cascades.

483 Yellow Poinciana (Yellow Flame Tree)

Peltophorum pterocarpum is a native of Northern Australia, though it is not found in the Wet Tropics area of Queensland except as an introduced flowering tree. It has a number of other common names, including **Copper Pod**, **Golden Flamboyant**, and **Yellow Flame Tree**. It reaches heights of from 8-15m, and forms a spreading crown. The leaves are bipinnate, meaning that the main stem of the leaf carries between 4 and 15 pairs of side stems, which in turn each carry 8 to 20 pairs of small leaflets, with rounded ends. They resemble some of the southern Wattles.

The flowers, which have a grape-like perfume, are carried on spikes which stand out from the foliage. The petals are from 10 to 20 mm long with frilly margins. Flowering is around Christmas time. The dark, wine red pods that follow are about 80mm long and eventually split in two lengthwise to release the seeds.

Found from SE Asia through to tropical Australia, this tree is widespread throughout the tropics. It is a weed in Tahiti and the roots can damage pavements.

Ornamental Trees

484 Native Crepe Myrtle

Lagerstroemia archeriana is the only Australian Crepe Myrtle, though there are about 50 species in Asia. The foliage is quite dense, and the tree is deciduous. The prolific pink or purple flowers grow on spikes above the foliage. The fruits are brown or blackish capsules and are eaten by Sulphur-crested Cockatoos. Several brown winged seeds are produced in each fruit.

Native Crepe Myrtle occurs in Cape York as far south as Chillagoe, as well as in WA, PNG and Indonesia. It is a plant of open forest. The original 'type' specimen was collected by a J.C. Baird on the Palmer River about 1883. In Australia this tree has been used, mainly in Queensland, as an ornamental street tree. It can be seen in Cairns and Innisfail where it makes a beautiful addition to the many introduced species on the streets.

Ht >15m   Lf 50-170mm   Fl Dec-Apr 30-50mm   Fr Feb-Aug 15-18mm

485 Pink Trumpet Tree

Tabebuia rosea is a striking street tree when in bloom, with masses of bright pink flowers on a leafless small tree. Originating from Central America, it is the national tree of El Salvador. The timber is valued for furniture wood and the Tabebuia family produces timber suitable for decking. While a large tree in its native habitat, the Pink Trumpet Tree is a modest sized street tree, losing its leaves and flowering during the dry season. (See also no 470).

Map of Region

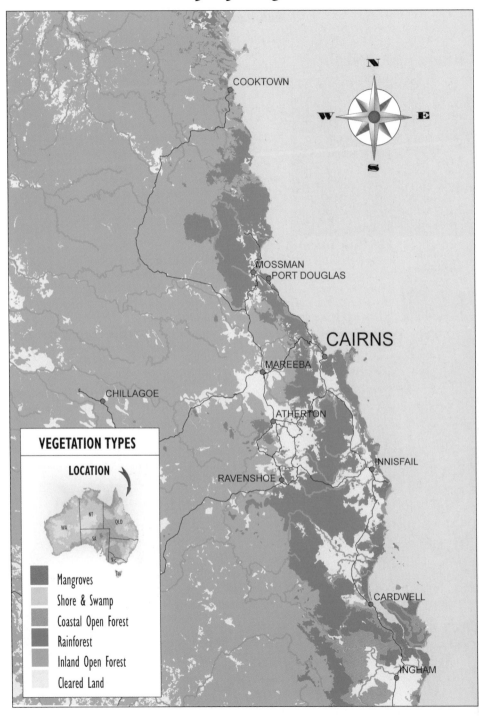

COOKTOWN

MOSSMAN
PORT DOUGLAS

CAIRNS

MAREEBA

CHILLAGOE

ATHERTON

INNISFAIL

RAVENSHOE

CARDWELL

INGHAM

VEGETATION TYPES

LOCATION

Mangroves
Shore & Swamp
Coastal Open Forest
Rainforest
Inland Open Forest
Cleared Land

Scientific Name Index

INDEX OF SCIENTIFIC NAMES (Page Numbers - not Plant Numbers)

Scientific Name Index

Scientific Name Index

PRIMITIVE PLANTS IN FAR NORTH QUEENSLAND

The tropical rainforests of North-east Australia include the highest concentration of primitive flowering plant families on Earth. Thirteen of the nineteen known families are represented here, and two are found nowhere else. This indicates that Australia's rainforests, far from being recent arrivals from Asia, as was once thought to be the case, are probably the 'oldest' rainforests on Earth. They have survived with less change than in other areas, preserved in refugia during periods of aridity, vulcanism, and the changes in sea level that accompanied the ice ages. They offer scientists an insight into the evolutionary history of plants that is not possible elsewhere.

Among the flowering plants considered primitive, the pollen of the rainforest vine *Austrobaileya scandens* closely resembles the most ancient pollen samples found. The other uniquely Australian family has only one member, the quite remarkable tree *Idiospermum australiense*. All other flowering plants are divided into two groups. Monocotyledonous plants have one seed leaf which emerges from the seed. These are mostly grasses and palms. Dicotyledonous plants produce two seed leaves - think of a bean seed, which splits into these two leaves. Only the Idiot Fruit can produce 3 or 4 seed leaves. Furthermore, it can grow multiple shoots from each seed. In this it is again unique. To our surprise, primitive plants often often appear far more complex than we would expect.

Australia hosts other, even older, forms of plant life, such as ferns, mosses and lichens. Kauri pines date back to the supercontinent of Pangaea, as do the Cycads, the link between the primitive ferns and flowering plants. The Zamia Palm has remained unchanged for 175m years. As well, the most primitive members of the large Proteaceae family occur here.

Common Name Index

INDEX OF COMMON NAMES (Page numbers-not plant numbers)

Common Name Index

Common Name Index